Roller Coaster Road

Traveling through tragedy toward a
destination of love and happiness

Tammy Ward

Roller Coaster Road

Editor: Rosalie Spaniel

Cover art by Estella @ www.99designs.com

Photo by Rick Norton @ rjnorton@fuse.net

Book design by MarzArts @ www.freelancer.com

ISBN 978-0-692-16760-1

ISBN (Ebook) 978-1-5323-8364-9

Printed in U.S.A.

The following is a story based on true-life events. Names and places have been changed to protect the privacy of those involved.

"Never give up on a dream just because of the

time it will take to

accomplish it. The time will pass anyway."

Earl Nightingale

TABLE OF CONTENTS

Prologue

Part I

Part II

This book is dedicated to my Mom, Dad and sister. Their lives inspired me to share our family's journey through a life-changing event.

PROLOGUE

I've come a long way from the shy little girl who searched for so many years for happiness and my own family to love and cherish.

The man of my dreams (we've been happily married for over 37 years) showed me how to have fun by living life to its fullest. We live in Charlotte, North Carolina, which fulfills my dream of escaping the cold, dreary northern weather.

As a parent, I always tried to inspire my two boys to do their best. I was fortunate to be a full-time mom to be there before and after school and be a part of their activities and sports. I'm still committed to supporting them as they begin to achieve their life goals – the one thing my Mom wasn't able to do for me. I know she loved me, but one night in October 1972, a part of her died. It took all her strength just to live one day at a time. But she couldn't be excited for me or inspire me to fulfill my dreams. I accepted that, but I promised myself I would always be there for my children.

I have never shared all the details of that fateful night. I was only fourteen and accepting this new family dynamic was difficult. Perhaps has been the reason I've shared only bits and pieces of my past, never the entire story. But now I wanted my family to know everything that happened and so I began to write this book. Once I began putting my thoughts on paper, the memories flowed out of me.

I was surprised I could remember so many happy childhood memories because the tragic ones have always been so vivid – like they happened yesterday. I also couldn't believe the relief I felt letting all these feelings, bottled up inside me for more than 40 years, out. Even today I sometimes have a hard time verbally expressing my feelings.

I hope reading this book will help others to persevere and never give up searching for happiness.

PART I

CHAPTER I
BACK IN TIME

Eric and I were leaving Charlotte, North Carolina, for Riverview, Ohio, for our quarterly visit to Eric's family. Although Eric and I grew up in Riverview, I haven't considered it home for over 20 years. Most people get excited to stroll down memory lane, but I dread every trip to my hometown.

As soon as we start heading north, the back of my neck starts to tighten, my smile becomes a frown and I get a knot in my stomach. Every day in Riverview something reminds me of the tragedy that changed my life more than 40 years ago. Being there just makes those haunting memories more vivid.

After more than seven hours, the tension in my neck has given me a pounding headache, which only worsens when I see the sign for the Greater Riverview Airport. Suddenly I'm eight years old and with my sisters, Julie, 10, and Karen, 15, bundled into the car on late, cold wintry nights when Mom drove to the airport to pick up Dad for his weekends home from his special project job in Boston, which lasted more than a year.

Dad was a mechanical engineer for Alco and worked on classified government contracts. He couldn't talk about them and I never thought much about his work until I was in my twenties. That's when I realized how difficult his work must have been because of hearing problems from childhood.

If his flight got in early enough, we would go up on the observation deck and watch the planes take off and land. Dad, the only family member who had flown, would tell stories about his flights.

8

I dreamed of someday being a flight attendant and flying around the world.

As I remember those times, I've come to appreciate how hard it must have been for Mom, who worked full time, to handle three girls while Dad was away. Mom had to arrange for our friends' stay at home moms to pick us up from school or drive us to and from swim team practices and other activities. Sometimes I was embarrassed because these moms were always transporting me. *I wished Mom could stay at home instead of working.*

"What are you smiling about?" Eric asks, bringing me back to the present.

"I'm just thinking about our trips to pick up my dad at the airport when we were little," I said, glancing out the window and realizing we were on the Suspension Bridge crossing from Kentucky to Ohio.

"Riverview has a pretty skyline, doesn't it?"

"Yes, it does." Eric was glad I had actually said something good about our hometown.

Crossing that bridge triggered another happy

memory – our annual summer vacation to Daytona Beach, after summer competitive swim season ended in mid-July. To get ready for our fourteen-hour ride to the beach, Dad would put plywood over the Oldsmobile's backseat and cushion it with blankets so we could stretch out. Nobody thought about using seatbelts in the 60s.

We always left shortly after daybreak to beat the rush hour traffic and take advantage of the cooler temperatures. We didn't have air-conditioning.

After a few hours on one particularly memorable trip, I asked Dad to make a bathroom stop. Dad liked to combine bathroom breaks with gas stops (one reason we had a cooler with drinks and food under the backseat board) and he said, "Just a little longer. We're making such good time, I don't want to stop."

About an hour later, he finally pulled into a Dairy Queen. I ran to the restroom while my sisters waited in line to order.

Julie and Karen were already eating their cones

when I went to the counter to order my favorite -
vanilla ice cream in a cup, dipped in chocolate.

I remember feeling lightheaded, but nothing
else until I came to, lying on the floor and seeing
Julie jumping up and down to get Mom or Dad's
attention. She never stopped licking her cone!

Dad quickly picked me up and the manager
rushed over. "Is she ok?" he asked, clearly concerned.

"I think she just needs something to drink,"
replied Dad.

Mom started yelling at Dad. "We should have
stopped sooner. From now on when we say we need
to stop, you have to stop!"

"Ok," Dad sheepishly replied.

When we got back in the car, Mom said, "Give
Sammy some room to stretch out."

"We're going to be squished," Julie complained.

I just smiled at this extra attention and laid my
head on the pillow. Usually Julie got all the attention.

I was fine by the time we got to Daytona
Beach. We always rushed to the beach as soon as

we arrived. We loved swimming in the ocean. Mom would lather us with baby oil and iodine to maximize our tans. Dad was 6'4" and would take us out to where the water was over our heads and hold our rafts until we could ride a perfect wave in. Mom loved to watch us ride the waves. It was always a fun-filled week.

Suddenly I realize we're driving through downtown Riverview past Holston's Department Store, where Mom worked. We'd go downtown several times a year to visit Mom there and I always felt special during those visits.

Mom started her career as a secretary. Eventually, through hard work and dedication, she became Executive Assistant to the Vice President of Operations, Mr. Nelson.

She was very popular and knew everyone. Whether you were a sales associate, in upper management, or on the cleaning crew, she was a friend. When Karen and Julie turned sixteen, she had no trouble getting them jobs. I declined Mom's offer to get me a job when I turned 16. After that fateful night, I wanted to go work where people didn't know our family's past.

But, growing up, I was always impressed with Mom's popularity. So many younger, up-and-coming employees, guys and girls, came to Mom for advice about their personal or work problems. She was a great listener and always gave her honest opinion, even when it wasn't the advice they hoped for. Julie was the same way. Her friends felt comfortable confiding in her and respected her advice. Julie didn't have many boyfriends, but boys often sought her advice about their girlfriends.

As we continued our drive through Riverview, I tried to focus on happy memories, thinking how our family differed from most 60s families. When Dad was home, he cooked and took us to school functions, swim practices, and organ or baton lessons. Mom didn't enjoy running us around or being involved in school activities. But she loved when we visited her on the one Saturday she worked each month.

On that day, we'd be up at 8:30 to say good-bye to Mom and place our breakfast orders. Dad never complained about fixing breakfast even when our egg orders were as different as our personalities.

I wanted a moon egg – just the yellow, no white. Like me, simple, definitely not a fancy. Karen always asked for fried eggs, also a simple request. Julie wanted a flat egg, beaten, but cooked flat – never scrambled. Like Julie, a little different, but not too different.

At Holston's, Mom would jump up and give us hugs and kisses. Mr. Nelson, only a few inches taller than our 5' Mom, always came out to say hello. When our lives turned upside down, Mr. Nelson helped Mom through those tough times. Dad never seemed to mind their close relationship. I think he was grateful for his help.

Here I go slipping back into those sad times. Please let me remember how much fun it was to see Mom especially our Christmas visits.

Christmas was a wonderful time at Holston's. Families from all over the area would come downtown to see the Christmas decorations. There was a different theme each year, but the main attraction was always Santa Land and the gift shop. To get to Santa, you had to walk through a winter wonderland maze with animated elf figures working in Santa's shop or children ice-skating on a frozen pond. I couldn't wait to get to the end to tell Santa my wish list.

Mom and Dad weren't surprised when Julie, always the tomboy, asked for an electric racecar track in 1963. My Santa's list was different - another baby doll and some troll dolls for good luck. Karen wanted books and new clothes.

Once Santa had our lists, we went to the gift store to buy presents for Mom and Dad and sneak a little something for each other, all neatly wrapped to be placed under the tree until Christmas.

Christmas was special, but every Saturday visit always ended with a walk across the street to an old-fashioned delicatessen with Formica countertops and swivel stools, which gave you a view of the cooks through the cutout in the wall. The restaurant was a favorite with Holston's employees, especially Mom. She was a close friend with the owner who always came over to say hello. Julie and Karen rushed to say hello; I always hid behind Mom.

When I finally come back from my Christmas memories, we're passing the sports stadium and I remember going to Knoch Field as a little girl to watch the Riverview Rangers – so long ago. I wanted to cling to those pleasant memories to keep the tragic ones away.

Dad loved baseball. He gave up his chance to play AAA ball at 19 when he enlisted in WWII. But he never lost his passion for the game and shared that passion with us. Mom didn't go with us, which looking back seemed strange. She liked watching baseball on TV. We just never questioned her about it.

But those games with Dad were memorable. We sat behind third base, right along the fence. During batting practice, we'd walk down to the field to collect autographs or maybe snag a practice ball.

Julie wore her baseball cap and took her glove, hoping to catch a foul ball. I wore a flowery skort with matching top and paid more attention to the people in the stands than to the game.

I was in sixth grade when a new stadium was built and my reward for getting straight A's was tickets to one of the first games. The seats were in the nosebleed section, but I didn't care. The next year, Dad and four coworkers purchased season tickets so we went to 20 games a year and our seats a lot better - eight rows from the field between home and first.

The Rangers dominated the League and our great seats definitely sealed my love of baseball. Mom even joined Dad at some games. I guess I remember that so vividly because it was one of the few times I saw Mom happy after the tragedy.

CHAPTER 2
THE THRILL RIDE

But happy memories only last so long and as we turned off the highway I braced myself, wondering which road Eric would take to his parents' house. He had several choices, but I only dreaded one. I prayed Eric wouldn't choose Franklin Road and was relieved when he turned up Liberty Avenue. I'd never asked him to avoid Franklin Road. I worried he'd think I was foolish. After all, it was a favorite with all the kids growing up, even me in grade school.

We called it roller coaster road because of the

four steep hills and I couldn't blot out memories of our Sunday outings along it. Dad never drove too fast, but it felt like the Oldsmobile flew over the pavement. Julie, Karen and I giggled as our bellies flopped – no seatbelts to keep us from bouncing up off the seat. Remembering how all three of us enjoyed such a simple thrill could even make me smile.

But then my thoughts drift to October 1972 and I see Julie in the new outfit I helped her pick out. Her friend, Gina was driving her dad's new Buick so there was enough room for Julie, Diane, Amanda, Gina, Vickie and Chris. They were on Franklin Road happy they had decided to go to a private party instead of the homecoming dance. I imagine them, not a care in the world, so happy just glad to be together.

Then in my head I hear a thunderous crash like two freight trains colliding. I picture tons of metal being mangled into an indistinguishable wreckage. I still pray none of them knew what hit them.

But we aren't on Franklin Road and I shake

my head to erase the memory of that night. No matter that 40 years have passed, my memories of what happened to Julie and her friends on roller coaster road are forever etched in my mind. My palms are sweaty and my heart is racing. I don't want Eric to know how upsetting these trips home are – or at least the impact it still has. I take a deep breath and come back to reality. These images come to mind so quickly and so vividly I wonder if I will ever be able to keep them away.

CHAPTER 3
FRIGHTENED BIRTHS

We're almost to our destination. *I should be able to keep it together until then.* Once we arrive, I'll pretend to be happy back in Riverview. But I know I will have to struggle to keep the memories from overwhelming me.

Eric wasn't part of my childhood although he was born and raised on Frost Lane, just down the street from where we lived until I was two. I don't have many memories of that time, but as we turn onto Frost Lane, I can hear Mom telling stories about when

Julie and I were born. Karen was five years old when Julie was born May 14, 1955. It was a shocking arrival. Mom would describe her tiny face, smashed from a breech birth and bluish-purple and yellow-green from the bruising, before declaring she was still beautiful. She and Dad couldn't have been prouder.

But Julie's medical problems didn't end with her birth. At six weeks she was diagnosed with pyloric stenosis, an enlargement of the muscles at the lower end of the stomach, which caused milk to shoot from her tiny mouth like an erupting volcano as soon as she finished nursing. I learned later this defect is four times more common in boys than girls and affects two to three infants out of 1,000. Even as a newborn, Julie was not part of the norm.

After describing the health problems, Mom always added that Julie quickly recovered from her bumpy beginning, growing into a happy, healthy little girl who slowly began to resemble Mom – the same green eyes, little pug nose and round face.

I always believed Julie's rough first months

created a special bond with Mom. I guess this was my way of trying to justify their closeness.

I also have vivid memories of my birth because of Mom's stories. That's how I know that sixteen months after Julie's birth, Mom and Dad were surprised to learn she was pregnant – and that this time, she'd say, Dad was hoping for a son to share his love of sports.

She and Dad were so busy caring for Karen and Julie, they didn't spend much time preparing for me. The pregnancy seemed normal, but Dad's sudden illness was not. Mom always described that evening as typical -- Dad enjoyed grilling as Julie and Karen played in the yard. But after dinner, Dad said he didn't feel well and went upstairs to lie down. The next morning, his fever was over 100 and he couldn't get out of bed. Mom called the family physician, and he said, "Take Henry to the hospital. I'll meet you there."

By midmorning, Dad was diagnosed with spinal meningitis and the doctor couldn't say how long he'd be in the hospital. That ended her stress free pregnancy. Mom visited daily, she had to be sure she didn't become exhausted as her due date approached. Neighbors and friends who volunteered to babysit would later say how amazed they were at Mom's strength. She never appeared overwhelmed or depressed.

Hearing how strong Mom was during this difficult time, I couldn't understand why she wasn't strong enough to deal with the accident.

Dad was hospitalized for six weeks, losing over seventy pounds, but came home fully recovered. Mom always talked about waiting impatiently for Grandpa to bring Dad home. When he got out of the car and Julie and Karen ran up to hug him, she was overjoyed and shocked at the sight of his emaciated body that her water broke!

The next few moments Mom said, were unbelievable. Grandpa got Dad to bed while Mom called neighbors to watch Julie, Karen and Dad. Then, she said, Grandpa gingerly put her into the car to return to the hospital.

With all the drama during the final months of her pregnancy, Mom and Dad hadn't discussed any names (I learned much later and if they had, they would've been boy's names. Dad really expected a son). When I arrived several hours later, on August 25, 1957, the newest member of the Neuman family, Mom called Dad to announce, "We have another girl! Now we need a name."

I remember that I smiled when I first heard how I got my name – and I still smile today. Mom said she was listening to Sammy Davis Jr. on the radio and immediately called Dad and said, "She should be Samantha, Sammy for short. Dad finally had a boy – or at least a boy's name.

Many years later when Dad finally told me he wanted a boy, it didn't matter then. I knew he was proud of me and loved me dearly. But I always felt the combination of Dad's illness and Mom's having to care for him and three girls, I probably didn't get as much attention as Karen and Julie in those very young years. I was never as confident as my sisters. Or maybe it was just insecurity that made me think that way.

CHAPTER 4
ALL AMERICAN FAMILY

Once we arrive at Eric's parents' house I can put my disturbing memories away for a little while. I don't remember much about our family's time in the bungalow on Frost Lane. By my second birthday, we had moved to a split-level home less than a mile from the bungalow.

That new house had three bedrooms (Julie and I shared one), a family room, living room, basement, and bigger yard. It was walking distance from the neighborhood swimming pool and swimming quickly became our favorite sport.

Most of our neighbors were also looking for more space for their growing families and we were soon part of the community. Julie and Karen were very outgoing. Julie especially rushed to meet our neighbors; I stayed by Mom's side.

Weekend cookouts with neighbors were the most fun, but even those happy times had some drama – like one Saturday cookout when Dad started his usual grilling ritual, pouring fluid on the charcoal. My jaw dropped when the flames shot skyward and some paper ash flew into my open mouth and burned my tongue. I was too shocked to cry out, but Julie was looking at me and when she saw the smoke coming out of my mouth she shouted," Hot ashes just flew in Sammy's mouth!" Even while she was yelling about me, she continued shoving potato chips into her mouth.

Dad grabbed the garden hose and sprayed water all over my face. Mom picked me up and gave me a big hug. I loved getting her attention. But what

I cherish most from that incident was realizing that Julie was looking out for me even when I didn't know it.

CHAPTER 5
BLUE RIBBON DAY

Even as I braced myself for the haunting memories I knew would return during our Riverview visit, I continued to think of all the happy times before the accident. One particularly memorable day stands out –a summer morning in 1962. Julie (7), Karen (10) and I were walking to the pool for my lessons and Julie and Karen's team practice. I loved swimming.

Julie and Karen were top swimmers in their age groups, but never bragged. Julie's favorite stroke was butterfly, one of the hardest to swim. It requires upper body strength. Julie was strong; she even beat the boys in arm wrestling. Karen swam freestyle. I was only four, but I was determined to be on the team.

That day my class had to dive off the one-meter board and swim to the ladder to earn a place on the team. When I got to the end of the board, I smiled at Julie and Karen, dove in and quickly swam to the pool edge where Julie and Karen were waiting to congratulate me.

I had two weeks to train for my first meet. I even got a new bathing suit, one designed to enhance performance, for the race. I felt like a torpedo shooting through the water in my new suit.

I was so excited! Mom and Dad were there to cheer me on and Julie and Karen made sure I knew when to line up for my event. I couldn't wait to swim and make them proud.

Finally! The 25-yard (one length of the pool) eight and under breaststroke was my chance for a ribbon. Even though the five other girls on the starting blocks were taller and three or four years older, I was ready to race.

The starter yelled, "Swimmers take your mark."

I crouched down in the ready position.

BANG! The gun went off. I dove into the water. As my head popped in and out of the water, the crowd's cheering made me swim faster.

I touched the wall and heard the roar of the crowd. Julie and Karen rushed over to congratulate me. I'd won my first blue ribbon – and began my competitive swimming career – at the age of four! Swimming would become my escape from the sorrow I felt after the accident.

CHAPTER 6
ANOTHER INJURY

Unpacking in my protective, neutral room on Frost Lane, I found myself recalling many other fond memories of my elementary years, especially playing school and sitting at the old wooden school desks in our basement. Karen was always the teacher, writing math and grammar questions on the big blackboard. Julie's hand always shot up faster than mine, but I didn't care. I was just happy to be playing with my sisters.

In nice weather, Julie played army or kickball

with the boys and Karen walked Shadow, our boxer. I played house with my Patty Play Pal doll or pushed Barbie and Ken around in their orange convertible. I was the happiest when Julie and I covered the family room floor with all the Barbie Dream House pieces.

During the winter months, Julie and I swam competitively. We practiced twice a week from six to eight p.m. and Dad always made sure we had a healthy meal before practice, including our favorite - a half-inch thick sirloin steak and fried potatoes. Not an acceptable meal before a workout these days!

On weekends, practice and weekend travel to Dayton or Louisville for swim meets, didn't leave much time for other activities, but Dad never complained about not having any time for him. He loved doing this for his three girls.

We seamlessly added a solid water activity to our winter program – ice-skating at a nearby farm where the low grassland turned into a shallow pond when the snow began to melt. It seemed to freeze overnight.

But the memory of one cold, sunny Saturday, after a week of below freezing temperatures, is like so many happy memories, tinged with sadness. I remember how we pleaded with Dad to take us skating and Mom bundling us up in our warmest coats, hats and gloves.

Dad always carefully laced our skates, making sure they were secure around the ankles. I can picture Julie and Karen immediately taking off. They had no fear. I tightly grasped Dad's hand as we slowly skated around the lake. Julie would whiz by to show me how much better she was. I always wanted to be like her some day. Eventually, I'd let go of Dad, but he was only an arm's length away.

The next day that happy memory faded as our family faced another problem. Julie woke complaining of a pain in her side. Mom shook it off as a pulled muscle from skating and put a heating pad on it.

When the pain worsened, Mom called the doctor. After hearing the symptoms, he said, "Meet me at my office right away." His diagnoses – appendicitis.

She needed surgery immediately before the inflamed appendix burst!"

Once again, Mom swung into action, making arrangements for Karen and me and getting Julie to the hospital. Later that evening we learned the operation was a success and Julie would be in the hospital a few days. On Monday her classmates made get well cards and sent them to the hospital. I was glad Julie was ok, but a little envious of all the attention she was getting from Mom, Dad, classmates and friends.

At Julie's follow-up visit, Mom and Dad learned if her appendix had ruptured, the outcome would have been tragic. But, they quickly erased that horrible thought from their minds and were just thankful for the happy outcome. When I thought of how well Mom and Dad handled Julie's appendicitis, I always wondered why she couldn't have been stronger when tragedy struck our family in 1972.

CHAPTER 7
ANIMAL HOUSE

Eric's parents don't have pets and strangely that always reminds me of the menagerie of cats and dogs we had. I didn't share the same emotional attachment with them as the rest of my family. They did comfort me when I was sad and needed unconditional love, but I never wanted any animals of my own and never formed a particular attachment to any of ours. Our dogs were treated more like furry people, than pets. The primary reason for my no-pets rule was of the heartache they brought to our family when one of them got hurt or had to be put to sleep because they were so sick. Mom would be depressed for weeks. *Why would I want to put myself in that situation?*

Mom had loved animals since she was a little girl, but didn't get her first pet – Mickey, a wire haired terrier, until after she and Dad were married. Dad grew up on a farm with cows, goats and chickens and had always loved animals.

Karen spent a lot of time at our grandparents' farm and, like Dad, always loved animals. Julie was such a caring person she relished tending to our dogs and cats. Any stray animals in the neighborhood ended up at our house; Mom or Julie brought them in to make sure they had food and shelter.

The first dog I remember was Suzette, our overweight French toy poodle. When Karen's friends came over, Suzette chased them, nipping at their toes until they had to jump on the couch. Unfortunately, Mom thought that was cute.

Charlie Brown, our wire-haired terrier, was

overly protective of family members – even when they weren't in danger. That led to quite a hassle one snowy New Year's Eve when Grandma was staying over. Mom brought home a stray Pekinese she'd found shivering out in the cold. There was no collar so Mom decided to keep him until the pound opened. When Julie named him Snoopy, I knew he'd be with us a lot longer than the weekend.

That night Charlie Brown took up his place next to Grandma on the couch. Snoopy, standing on his hind legs, placed his front paws on the couch, Charlie Brown quickly attacked Snoopy, damaging his eye. The result – Mom and Dad drove over 20 miles on a snowy night to get Snoopy's eye repaired. And he wasn't even our dog!

A few hours and several hundred dollars later, they came home, and we adopted him, although his vision in the damaged eye was a problem. Several months later we reluctantly gave him away because he was a perfect companion for a friend's elderly mother.

When I think about all the dogs we had, those two and Crissy, a 2-1/2 lb. Yorky, stand out. Crissy was Mom's baby after the accident, her only spark of life. Crissy was devoted to Mom. I believed she would die of a broken heart if anything happened to Mom.

CHAPTER 8
DREAM HOUSE

It's impossible to keep the memories – happy and sad - out of my mind when I'm in Riverview. Mom's dream house is always part of that nightmare – it would become the house of sorrow.

When Mom and Dad decided we needed a bigger house, Mom found a new development less than five minutes from our house. We eagerly watched our beautiful, brick, two-story house take shape - four bedrooms, a family room with a fireplace, a bigger kitchen for Dad, and a huge backyard that backed up to a golf course. It definitely fulfilled Mom's wishes.

We'd be in the same schools – I'd continue with my classmates in third grade, Julie and her classmates moved up to fifth grade and Karen, now a rising sophomore, just added to her circle of friends. We were still swimming competitively and also joined a swim and tennis club, which was an easy walk after Dad cut a path through a vacant wooded area.

During the summer swim season, we lived at the pool from 8 to 5. My new best friend, Lori Bonner, was also on the swim and tennis teams. After workouts, Lori and I helped with the preschool swim lessons, teaching toddlers how to blow bubbles and kick their feet. After lunch, we'd play cards, swim, or dive from the boards. By 5:00 I was ready to go home.

But I could never remember that glorious time when our house was full of love and happiness – when I was so busy enjoying life and making happy memories -- without thinking how that world ended so abruptly. The dark cloud that would cover our house and family is never far from my memory.

One of my happy/sad memories during the first year in our new home came during a swimming meet. I was one of the fastest breaststroke swimmers in my age group and as the city finals, a wrap-up competition for all the district teams, approached I was determined to prove I was the best.

After the Saturday morning time trials, the fastest eight swimmers in the individual heats would compete in the Sunday final events. On Saturday when the 25-meter girl's breaststroke was called for my age group, I approached the sign-in table with a flip-flopping stomach and pounding heart. But my nerves disappeared when I saw that I'd beaten the seven other swimmers in past meets. On the starting block, I said to myself, "I can do this."

The starting gun sounded and we were off. I heard the crowd roar as my head popped out of the water. A quick glance left and right showed the other swimmers in line with me so I pulled harder, dunking my head into the water to make one final stroke to the wall. I came in first – and beat the city record!

Coach, Dad and Lori raced over to congratulate me as I climbed out of the pool, but then one of the officials walked over and said, "Sammy, your hands weren't parallel when you touched the wall."

"What does that mean?" I asked. I knew my hands had to touch at the same time, but not that they had to be parallel.

"You're disqualified." He turned and quickly walked away.

I couldn't believe it.

It didn't take long for everyone at the swim club to hear about my disqualification. The next day, Coach and my swimming buddies congratulated me on a great swim and gave me a trophy with a handmade inscription, "Sammy, the Champ." I may not have won the event, but I did win with my friends!

CHAPTER 9
SOCIAL LIVES

We'd only been in Riverview a few days, but I'd already relived most of my childhood just by driving by so many familiar places. I couldn't help myself from thinking how quickly those years flew by. Remembering how intrigued I was with Karen's teenage friends and their busy lives. Julie was technically a teenager too, but her friends weren't nearly as interesting.

I always admired how Mom made people, teenagers and young adults, feel comfortable talking with her. Thinking about those happy times, I can almost forget that night –until we pass a group of teenagers and my memory turns to how Mom's conversations ended after the accident.

But during those happy years, I couldn't wait to be like my sisters and have a lot of friends to hang out with. I wished I could hang around with them, dreamed about how they'd want to be with me when I got a little older. I never imagined how different my teenage years would be. How could I?

When Julie was thirteen, she seemed to spend more time with her friends and their families than ours. She was like Mom. They just made people feel at ease so everyone liked being around them. They never judged anyone; they just accepted them.

Gina was Julie's best friend for a while, but a couple years later Gina got a steady boyfriend and their friendship faded. I hoped Julie would turn to me for companionship, but she started hanging out with Patti, a neighbor friend, and quickly became a frequent visitor at their house.

Karen was very popular at school and work and our house was a gathering place for all her friends, especially the boys. It was easy to see why. She could carry off an eye-catching hot pants outfit and white knee-high boots like nobody else.

If Karen wasn't home, her guy friends would still come over to talk to Mom. They called her Myrtle. I wasn't sure how she got that name; I thought it might be because she was short and round like a turtle's shell. I think they were drawn to her because she would give them honest advice about any topic – sex, parents, drinking, whether they liked her comments or not.

Ironically, I was afraid to discuss just about any topic with Mom and I really don't know why. I'd write her notes – even for simple requests like sleeping over at Lori's or going to the mall. She'd find notes on the kitchen counter or her dresser in the bedroom: *Dear Mom, can I please, please, please go over to Lori's tonight? Dad already said it was ok. So please, please can I go?* I'd always be out of sight when she read it.

"Don't you think you spend too much time over Lori's house?" she'd always ask once she found me.

"No. Mrs. Bonner doesn't mind." I'd always reply.

Once I got permission, I'd give her a peck on the cheek and run off to pack my suitcase.

Even though I didn't have the easy relationship with Mom that Karen and her friends had – or the special bond between Mom and Julie – I had a great life during these years. Karen's outgoing personality ensured a continuous flow of boyfriends during her college years while she worked part-time at Holston's. She was one of the top associates in the men's department.

Mom made sure Karen met all the eligible single men at Holston's, especially one named Bob. Mom persuaded him to take Karen to dinner. When Karen ordered a Coke, Bob realized she wasn't even 21. Since he was 26 that ended any dating although they remained friends.

But Mom didn't give up hope and a few years later they started dating regularly and Bob became a permanent fixture for holidays or Sunday dinner. They married shortly after her 21st birthday. Julie and I were so excited for Karen, but mostly we were excited to be in our first wedding.

Even my memories of this joyous occasion are somewhat bittersweet – and once again – being in Riverview brought it all back. Passing Holston's, where we bought Karen's gown and our bridesmaids dresses, I remember how excited I was at the beginning of that shopping trip. It was a November wedding, we chose gowns with a maroon velvet empire-waist (a perfect fall color) and a taffeta floral overlay on the silk full-length bottom. They were beautiful and Julie's dress fit perfectly.

Then I slipped into the smallest size and my heart sank. There was no way to alter the dress to properly fit my small, flat chest. I'd have to wear a padded bra! I was emabarrassed, but that turned out all right when everyone commented how grown-up I looked. I still wish I had Julie's figure.

Karen and Mom spent countless hours planning the wedding and reception. More than 200 people (mostly Holston employees) attended the ceremony and reception. I remember Mom and Dad dancing and looking so happy.

Shortly after they married, Bob took a promotion with Holston's and they moved to Lexington. I never had the opportunity to develop a close relationship with Karen because of the age difference, but I would still miss her.

PART II

CHAPTER 10
HOMECOMING OR COMING HOME?

There's no way to avoid Marion High School when we're in Riverview – and no way to block my memories. They're such a jumble – happy, sad, never really resolved – and always among the most vivid when I'm back.

I was so happy at the beginning of my sophomore year. School was the one place I excelled, easily surpassing Julie. But mostly I was looking forward to this year because Julie, now 17 and a senior, no longer seemed to consider me an annoyance. We were actually developing a sisterly friendship and that's why my excitement about my first high school homecoming had nothing to do with the big game or the other homecoming activities.

The only thing on my mind was going shopping with Julie after school – a dream come true. She was so cool, confident, and friendly with many different people – girls on the drill team, boy and girl athletes, and even students who weren't among the most popular crowds. Everyone was a friend. I just wanted to be her pal – going out to eat or shop or go to a movie.

I knew I'd miss Julie after her graduation, so I was determined to take full advantage of our developing closeness while I could.

Julie had already been accepted into the four-year business program at the University of Riverview and often seemed more interested in that – and her job at Holston's – than high school. Her big decision now was deciding whether to live at home and commute or live on campus. I knew, no matter what she decided, that college would change our relationship so I sometimes begged her to include me – even in mundane activities like running up the street for milk or visiting a friend. A typical conversation might go something like this:

"Please let me go with you," I'd plead.

"No, stop bugging me. I don't have to take you everywhere I go!" she'd shout.

"Why not? I'm going to tell Mom."

"Go ahead, I don't care."

I usually didn't complain to Mom – just sulked in my room.

But the Friday of homecoming, she actually asked me to go shopping with her. I got off the bus and ran home because I knew Julie would already be there. I didn't want to jeopardize my shopping date by being late.

When she yelled, "Come on Sammy, let's go!" I jumped off my bed, ran down the stairs and headed out the door. I knew she wouldn't leave without me, but I wasn't taking any chances.

Julie had started working as a part-time sales associate at Holston's downtown when she turned 16. She loved working in the designer department and her boss was impressed with her ability to build a loyal customer base. She was definitely no longer that tomboy who hated to wear dresses. I envied her ability to coordinate outfits and looked forward to her giving me advice. She looked great in all the latest fashions.

Since we didn't have much time, we went to the neighborhood shopping center. I ran back and forth from the dressing room to the sales floor for about an hour, happy to be waiting on Julie and she seemed grateful for my assistance. She finally decided on a red, green, and yellow plaid blazer and a green cable sweater, which I hoped to borrow someday although I knew it would never look as good on me.

I took after Dad's side of the family – tall, thin and very flat chested. Mom told everyone, "Sammy's legs start under her armpits." In sixth grade, my hair was cut very short to look like Twiggy, that year's most popular model. Apparently there was no resemblance. Once when I was shopping with Karen, a friend, who had came up to talk to her seemed puzzled. Finally, she said, "I didn't know you had a little brother."

No wonder I had a figure complex!

Julie was well endowed and looked the most like Mom – muscular arms and legs from swimming butterfly and not an ounce of flab on her body. Her small-boned frame emphasized her womanly attributes, but she never tried to show off her figure, choosing pullover, crew-neck sweaters over plunging necklines. *If I had a figure like that, I'd show it off!*

When we drive past the high school stadium, which happens too many times during our visit, I remember Julie looking fashionable in her new outfit leaving for the football game with her friend, Amanda. Dad dropped me off to meet my girlfriends.

My girlfriends and I talked to classmates and walked behind the packed stands to talk with the boys, paying no attention to the score. Julie and Amanda stopped by, but quickly moved on, but I didn't care after my wonderful afternoon with her.

Later, curled up in bed, I recapped my unforgettable day before I fell asleep. I wouldn't hear Julie come in, but I knew Mom wouldn't sleep until she got home at 12:30. Julie never missed her curfew, but Mom never fell asleep until she was safely at home.

It's always painful to remember that happy evening because of the tragedy that followed – especially since that Saturday morning hinted at that night's events. Mom, Dad and I were already at the kitchen table when Julie came down ready to go to work. After she finished breakfast, Julie stayed to tell Mom her plans for the evening. She wasn't going to the homecoming dance because she was going to a party with Amanda, Vickie, and Diane and "Gina is who is driving."

Mom didn't seem happy with the plans. "I don't mind you're going with Amanda, Vickie and

Diana, but Gina only comes around when her boy-friend is busy," she said.

"That is not true, Mom," Julie defended Gina. "I'm glad Gina will be with us."

Things were still a little strained at dinner and Julie quickly ate her steak, fried potatoes and salad, one of her favorite meals. Mom didn't bring up her reservations about Gina, but her displeasure was obvious.

Mom and I were watching TV when Julie came down dressed for her night out. She looked ter-rific in her A-Smile jeans and the sweater and blazer I'd helped her select. Her golden blonde hair flowed smoothly down the middle of her back, slightly curled on the ends. But she seemed worried.

"What's wrong?" I asked.

"I can't find my $20," she said. Losing $20 was a big deal to someone working part-time for $1.75/hour; it didn't help when Mom yelled, "You lost $20? How can you lose money?"

"I cashed my paycheck and counted it before

leaving the bank, but maybe I didn't get the right amount." Julie tried to explain. It didn't seem likely Julie would lose her money (she was always very careful with money) and I tried to reassure her that it would turn up.

Mom didn't have any reassuring words for Julie about the money, probably because she still wasn't happy with Julie going out with Gina. When the car horn honked about 8:30, Julie mumbled "good-bye" and left without her usual kiss for Mom.

I'd been feeling jealous because Julie was going out and looked so great, but I felt a tinge of happiness when Mom and Julie had this little spat. I would regret that momentary sentiment, but it was just so rare that they butted heads I couldn't help myself. I was insecure and lacked the confidence to be more outgoing and I couldn't help thinking Julie was Mom's favorite.

After Julie left, Mom sat in the chair knitting but every time I looked up from the TV I could see the tension on her face. I knew she was upset over how she handled Julie misplacing her money and friendship with Gina. Mom would never forgive herself for that overreaction and the missed good-bye kiss. By 10, we turned off the TV and went to bed.

CHAPTER 11
THE STRANGER AT THE DOOR

As a child, I seldom had trouble falling asleep and sleeping peacefully through the night, unlike later nights and the nights during our visits to Eric's parents. That tragic night was no different. Dad's hearing loss allowed him to sleep soundly, but I knew Mom slept fitfully until Julie was home safely, waking at even the slightest noise. But that night a loud knock around midnight woke me. I panicked. *Who is this intruder?*

If only it had been an intruder. Instead it was a stranger whose chilling words on that starry Saturday night of October 20, 1972, would change our lives forever.

Mom passed my room quickly and I followed her, crouching on the landing and leaning as far forward as possible without losing my balance. I could only distinguish a man's silhouette, but I could hear the conversation.

"Is your husband home?

"What do you want?" Mom questioned.

"Please, I need to speak with your husband," he compassionately said.

Mom was adamant, even as her voice rose in panic. "Officer, what do you need to talk to my husband about? I want to know!" Not a stranger, a police officer, and I remember a feeling of dread coming over me.

"Ma'am, I'm terribly sorry; there's been an accident involving your daughter."

With those words, my life changed completely.

They robbed me of my Mom and they continued to haunt me on our home visits for many years.

I remember my Mom's horrific, blood-curdling, ear-piercing, unimaginable scream rising from deep within her. I started to stand, but my movements seemed in fast-forward and slow motion at the same time.

I will never forget that scream. Later, Patti, Julie's friend from two houses down, told me she heard the scream through closed windows. She thought it was an animal in extreme agony.

I ran to wake up Dad, but all I could think of was Mom's reaction to the officer's words. I didn't wait for Dad to dress. I rushed downstairs. Mom was lying on the living room floor screaming, "No, no, no, Julie, Julie, Julie!"

Since I still didn't know how devastating the news was, I simply asked the officer, "What should I do?

Tears welled up in his eyes and he mouthed, "I'm so sorry," while he radioed for an ambulance for Mom. She was in shock.

When Dad came down, the officer took him to the kitchen to tell him his seventeen-year-old daughter had been killed. The only thing we learned that night was that two boys had crashed into the car Julie was in – nothing about her friends.

I reached down to hold Mom and felt the flesh on my left thigh rip open. Our wire-haired terrier had leaped up to protect Mom, attacking me. In pain and anger, I yanked his collar and dragged him to the basement.

I tried to ease Mom's pain, but it was hopeless. Her grief was indescribable. The only words that could stop her pain would never be said. And we couldn't even deal with our grief alone. The officer said someone would have to identify Julie's body and asked if there was a close family friend who could go to the morgue with Dad. The police weren't able to identify the victims because driver's license didn't have photos.

The only person Dad could ask to do this

gruesome task was his dearest friend, Roy Gibson, who lived down the street. Julie was like a daughter to the Gibsons. She babysat their two children and often relied on them for advice about college, working and relationships.

I called Mr. Gibson at 12:45 and he came within minutes. When his efforts to console Mom failed, he turned to Dad, holding him in his arms and crying with him. In a few minutes, he realized that neither Mom nor Dad could think clearly enough to call Karen and Bob in Lexington. He made the call and then waited with us for the ambulance.

I laid next to Mom on the living room floor, holding her close to try to stop the uncontrollable convulsions. The ambulance finally arrived and they lifted her onto the stretcher. Dad would meet her at the hospital after going to the morgue to perform the worst duty that any parent could do. I would go to the Gibson's house.

I learned later that Dad couldn't enter the room to identify the body. Mr. Gibson went in. The morgue visit was never mentioned again.

At the Gibson's, I laid down in the guest room, but I couldn't rest. My stomach was like a twisted rope and my head was ready to explode. I lay there petrified in the dark, quietly crying. *This had to be a terrible nightmare.*

CHAPTER 12
HEADLINE NEWS

Sometimes when I wake up on Frost Lane, I'm suddenly back to that October morning when I woke early, still dazed, and left the Gibson's, stopping to pick up the paper in our driveway. Our house was eerily quiet although I knew Mom and Dad were upstairs.

Mrs. Gibson had told me Dad called late last night and said Mom would be heavily sedated to get her through these next few days. I wasn't quite sure what that meant, but I said ok. I was glad I didn't have to face them. *I just wasn't ready. What would I say to Mom and Dad?*

And I certainly wasn't ready for the front page. Julie's senior picture and pictures of Amanda, Chris, Vickie and Diane were splashed across the page, next to the images of two mangled cars that looked more like heaps of scrap metal than cars. Not even the make and model could be identified. The article read:

Airborne Car Carries Death to
Five Area Teenagers

The five Marion High School girls and their 18-year old male rider had apparently never met Dean Patterson or James Donley until they met so tragically about 10:30 p.m. Saturday.

It had been a pretty good weekend for Marion High. The Warriors had beaten Parkwood 35-21 in the annual homecoming football game on Friday. The homecoming dance was Saturday night, but the girls had opted for the party instead of the dance.

Gina Hamilton was driving and had taken

her family's new Buick, with only 230 miles on it instead of her Mustang because she had so many riders. On their way they stopped to pick up Chris Thompson, a hitchhiker whom they recognized as a former Marion student.

Dean Patterson and James Donley had been close friends for a couple years and were "just out riding around," James's mother said. They were probably going home. James was supposed to be home at 11 p.m. and was already a half hour late.

As the girls and their male passenger reached the intersection of Crane and Franklin Rds., the Patterson car came flying through the air, smashing the whole right side of the new Buick and killing five of the six teenagers in the car.

The dead are: Miss Diane Boyar, 17, daughter of William D Boyar Jr. Miss Vickie Zimmerman, 17, daughter of Mr. and Mrs. Thomas Zimmerman. Miss Amanda Fisher, 17, daughter of Mr. and Mrs. Stephen Fisher, Miss Julie Neuman, daughter of Mr. and Mrs. Henry Neuman, and Chris Thompson, 18, son of Mr. and Mrs. Dwight Thompson.

The three other youths involved in the crash were taken to St. Marion Hospital. The Patterson youth, 16, was listed in fair condition with head and facial lacerations and two broken ankles. The Donley youth, 15, was listed in fair condition with head and facial cuts. Gina Hamilton, 17, was listed as fair with a laceration at the base of her skull.

County police said the Patterson car was apparently traveling at a high speed on Franklin Rd. As the car went over a dip in the road, it went airborne for 108 feet, landed and skidded 262 feet into a utility pole and then went airborne again, hitting the other car in the intersection, police said. After hitting the Hamilton car, the Patterson car skidded for another 26 feet, police reported.

Police said the accident is still under investigation, but would not say whether charges against Patterson were likely.

Life squads from Monford, Union and Chester responded to the scene of the accident and to free the injured and the dead from the wreckage. A Monford squad man said that torches couldn't be used to cut away the wreckage because gasoline tanks on the autos erupted.

The superintendent of Marion Schools said that a memorial service would be held at the high school. The senior class will meet to try to find an answer to the questions, "How can we make it a memorial for the living so that this tragedy isn't a complete waste?" he said.

The article in the paper was accurate. It had all the facts – except the ones that really mattered. It couldn't report how the lives of the families who lost their loved ones would be forever transformed.

CHAPTER 13
ROLLER COASTER ROAD

I can remember how I reacted to the article as if it was yesterday. I threw the paper down. This couldn't be about Julie and her friends. *She couldn't be gone.*

I remembered the fun we had on Franklin Road when we were little, riding up and over each hill on our roller coaster road. Even though Dad never drove too fast, it still felt like the car lifted off the pavement and we were flying over each hill. Julie and I always giggled as our bellies flopped. *I will never go on that road again.*

And then I remember tears – and they still come when I'm back in Riverview. I remember thinking Julie, Diane, Amanda, Gina, Vickie and Chris were probably laughing, happy spending the evening together rather than going to the homecoming dance. I can see Julie making a model's turn at the bottom of the steps to let me admire the outfit I'd helped her pick out. I remember thinking there would have been no warning of the horror about to happen.

And next I remember came the anger as I imagined the two boys in the other car, laughing about their success in buying beer at the delicatessen – just cruising around drinking. I imagined them speeding up as they drove up and down the hills, reaching for that rush which I enjoyed as a child. Were they so drunk they didn't know how fast they were going?

Now Julie, Amanda, Vickie, Diane and Chris were dead. Why did they have to lose their lives so senselessly? How could Dean and James escape with only minor injuries? Will we ever be able to get through this?

CHAPTER 14
THAT'S WHAT FRIENDS ARE FOR

Even when we don't drive on roller coaster road, we often pass the intersection and Eric always teases me about drawing into a shell. He senses something is wrong, but can't quite figure it out. Of course, he knows about Julie's death. This catastrophe, the worst accident in Chester County history, shocked the entire community. Even close friends and neighbors were at a loss and struggled to find the words and gestures to comfort the grieving families.

So they brought food for comfort –more food than any family could eat, especially since the last thing we wanted to do was eat. Even the sight of food made me sick. Food would not fill the hole in our hearts.

Although we understood the sympathy behind these caring actions, it was difficult to even acknowledge, much less convey our appreciation. Instead our family withdrew during those first unbearable days.

I knew Mrs. Bonner, my best friend Lori's mother, had called several times in the days following the accident – as had Lori, but I didn't talk to them. I couldn't bring myself to reach out to anyone.

But on the day of the viewing, I remember we needed help desperately.

Dad and I showered and dressed for the long day ahead, but Mom just laid in bed, crying and refusing to get up.

"I can't go, I just can't do it!" she cried.

"Please Mom, we have to say good-bye to Julie," I begged.

Dad tried to lift her, but she went rigid,

stiffening her body and Dad finally gave up. While we were struggling with this emotional turmoil, the doorbell rang and I ran downstairs. Mrs. Bonner was standing there. *We hadn't called for help. How did she know we desperately needed someone to rescue us?*

She simply took me in her arms.

"Mom won't get out of bed," I sobbed.

"Sammy, take your father downstairs," she commanded. "I'll take care of your mother."

Thirty minutes later, Mom was in the shower. Mrs. Bonner stayed to help her dress and put on make-up. When they slowly walked into the kitchen, Mom's hair was nicely styled and her make-up hid the puffiness around her eyes. She wore a simple black dress and appeared calm –almost eerily calm. But it didn't matter. My grief-stricken mother was going to tackle the hardest day of her life. I never asked Mrs. Bonner how she performed this miracle, but I'm still forever grateful for her unconditional caring presence that day.

CHAPTER 15
DEATH MARCH

Thinking of the joyous time, almost a year ago, of Karen's wedding and how vibrant and beautiful Julie looked in her bridesmaid dress only heightened my grief. It was unimaginable to see Julie, in that dress, as her lifeless body laid in the metallic rose coffin. Her flaxen hair flowed onto the satin pillow hid the trauma to her head. It's a picture I can't erase and I know will haunt me at some point during our visits back to Riverview.

I will never forget how full the funeral home

was. Classmates, teachers, Mom and Dad's coworkers, neighbors, my friends, extended family, and many unfamiliar faces whose lives Julie had touched waited to pay their respects to a wonderful young woman. Many of these same people would soon attend four other services for Julie's friends.

Mom sat in a small area next to the visitation room. Julie's casket was clearly visible, and viewers could clearly hear Mom's heart-wrenching cries as they entered the parlor. Karen, Dad and I stood in the visitation room and talked with the visitors.

Some mourners stood silently as if trying to make sense of this tragedy. Others formed groups and chatted; many wept openly. A number left without approaching Mom, not knowing what to say. Julie's friend, Patti, almost fainted when she placed her hand on Julie's cold hand. I wondered how she had the courage to make that gesture. I hadn't even mustered the courage to walk up to the casket and look at Julie's body.

Of all my memories, this evening is the most

clouded. I don't remember how long we stood to accept the heartfelt condolences or even who left last. I only remember being totally exhausted mentally and physically; we all went silently to bed.

CHAPTER 16
GOING THROUGH THE MOTIONS

I always hoped we'd have good weather when we visited Riverview. Of course, we didn't on this trip. I woke midway in our visit to the same bone-chilling wind of Julie's funeral day - just a week before at homecoming we had enjoyed spring-like weather.

Suddenly I'm back struggling to select an outfit for the services and thinking that the dreary weather was fitting for this somber occasion. I remember wondering why black was the appropriate outfit. *That seems too depressing.* I finally compromised and selected a brown, ribbed turtleneck and dark brown tweed skirt. Julie would have approved.

The house was quiet, unlike all the commotion over the past week. Mom and Dad were already dressed and downstairs having coffee. I was relieved we wouldn't be reliving yesterday's turmoil.

Mom and I moved our scrambled eggs around on the plates. Even Charlie Brown, lying beside Mom's chair, sensed the emotional tension. No one spoke. I still was finding it difficult to believe Julie was going to be buried today and wondering how we all would get through our last private visit with Julie before everyone arrived for the service. I was glad Bob and Karen would be meeting us at the funeral home – less pressure on me.

The number of people who returned for the service overwhelmed Karen and me. The ceremony included several eulogies that touched everyone. Mom, completely exhausted, wept throughout the service, but not hysterically. My eyes burned from the tears I'd shed the past few days.

As the mourners moved to the cars, we were again alone with Julie. I stood by myself at the back of the room still not believing what was happening. As the directors prepared to close the casket, I saw Mom dart forward.

"Please No! No! No! Oh, my Julie!" Mom begged.

One of my most vivid memories of that day I will never forget was when Dad and two of the funeral directors had to pry Mom away from the casket and drag her to the limo. I felt nauseous and was grateful Karen and Bob took me to their car so I didn't have to endure the agony in Mom and Dad's limo. I couldn't believe it when I saw over 75 cars line up for the police escort to the cemetery.

At the cemetery, dark clouds threatened; I wrapped my coat around me. Dad tightly held Mom to keep her legs from buckling as they walked to the gravesite where more than a hundred people gathered, all with the same look of disbelief and sadness on their faces.

This cemetery, one of the most scenic in Riverview, seemed park like with its rolling hills, huge oak trees, and ponds scattered throughout. Julie's gravesite was at the top of a hill overlooking a valley and included the plots Mom and Dad had purchased so they would be next to her forever.

Dad was still holding Mom in his arms. Bob was embracing Karen. I stood next to Dad wishing someone would comfort me. Patti was with her family, standing some distance from us, and must have sensed my despair. She whispered to her brother and he walked over and gently put his arm around me. Tears started streaming down my face. They were for Julie, but also for me. I was finally being comforted.

The serene setting did nothing to ease the sadness of the crowd. When the minister finished, people began returning to their cars. I stood frozen, listening to Mom's agonizing shrill cries. When I could finally move, I held onto Patti's brother and slowly walked back to the car. I couldn't bear to look back to see Mom's final good-bye to Julie.

The house was filled with relatives, neighbors, friends and coworkers when we returned from the cemetery. I was there physically, talking and hoping I was saying the right things, but I felt nothing. *Would all these people remember Julie a few months from now?* Their lives would go on as usual, but ours would always be consumed with grief. Our daily routines would never return to normal. *How could we ever recover from this?*

CHAPTER 17
ONE DAY AT A TIME

I don't always know what will trigger a memory when I'm in Riverview, passing Julie's favorite restaurant, driving by the high school or just the weather. But driving by the cemetery is always an emotional knockout I remember every detail of that final day and I wish we had been able to move beyond the funeral and begin living again. That didn't happen.

A week after Julie's funeral, Mom and Dad went back to work; I went back in school. We struggled to regain some sense of normalcy, but we knew our daily routines would never be the same. Her work was now her lifeline – her only motivation to get up every morning and live another day.

I was glad to get back into my school routine. At least schoolwork took my mind off the tragedy. But coming home to an empty house only increased my loneliness and sadness. I was afraid to be alone and asked Mom if I could stay with the Gibson's after school.

I quickly adjusted to this new routine; I'd found a comfort zone. Hanging out with a cheerful family helped me cope with the quiet, solemn atmosphere at home. My afternoons were filled with laughter and wonderful conversations with Mrs. Gibson. I could talk to her about school, girls and boys, things that no longer interested Mom.

But even those times were never completely free from sorrow like one afternoon, Mrs. Gibson told me Dad visited Julie's gravesite every day, sometimes often both at lunch and after work. I was almost physically sick thinking how awful it would be to sit at the gravesite just looking at Julie's name on the stone. *Why didn't he ever tell me? I can't imagine how painful it must have been.* And I wondered if that's why he poured himself a drinking glass size of vodka when he came home.

Many years later when I visited the gravesite, I realized Julie's birthdate on the headstone was wrong. I could only hope Mom and Dad were so distraught every time they visited they never realized it.

After a few months, our days were settled into a pattern. Dad starting dinner so we could eat when Mom, who would be exhausted, got home. I knew there would be no laughter and little conversation at dinner because Mom's antidepressants would have worn off, so I left the Gibson's house reluctantly.

We all missed Julie's dinnertime stories, especially when she talked about work and Mom would add interesting tidbits. Julie was such a good storyteller, I use to be mesmerized by her stories. Mine never seemed that interesting; I rarely talked at dinner, just happy to listen to Julie. After her death, it was just a relief to get through dinner and another day.

The after-dinner routine never varied. I'd clean up the dishes, Dad retreated to his room and Mom hurried to her bedroom to pop sleeping pills and end another day. Alone again, I'd sit at the kitchen table, finish my homework and watch some TV before turning in for the night.

I continued to stay at the Gibson's after school for several months, clinging to the only happy time in my life. I was soon spending weekend time there, and attending Sunday church with them. I remember sitting in the pew listening to the priest's sermon and hoping to find an answer to the questions I couldn't erase from my mind. *Why did this happen to us? Will we ever be happy again? Will the ache in my heart ever heal?* Week after week there were no answers, I finally ended my church visits.

CHAPTER 18
BEHIND CLOSED DOORS

Once the memories start, every moment alone becomes a time to relive that difficult time. I eventually stopped going to the Gibson's after school, but I continued to search for answers and every time we drove past a small chapel on the bus ride home from school, I thought about stopping in. I wondered if I might find someone who might help me deal with losing Julie, my depressed Mom and Dad's sorrow.

I never went in. Mom continued to question belief in God because she couldn't understand how

God could have let Julie die so young. Going to the chapel would have seemed like a betrayal. And how could I go to church to try to find belief when I had doubts, too?

Instead I went home and sneak into Julie's room for comfort before Mom and Dad got home. Dad had closed Julie's bedroom door the night of the accident; it remained off limits, but my secret visits continued for some time.

Julie's bedroom faced the front of the house and the sun lit up the room. Her canopy bed had always been my favorite, but now I was too scared to ask Mom if someday it could mine. Her room was simple, like Julie. Everything had its place - her silver jewelry box on her dresser, her clothes and shoes neatly arranged in her closet, and the brush with matching hand mirror angled perfectly on her dresser – all frozen in time, exactly as she left it that fatal night.

I remember thinking Julie's room showcased the beautiful young lady she had become. The

French provincial furniture and canopy bed mirrored her feminine transformation for her earlier tomboy days. But there was a feeling of lifelessness about the room and I could never keep a chill from slowly creeping down my spine. There were also feelings of guilt when I opened the door. *Was I intruding on something that was not supposed to be tampered with?* But those feelings always gave way to comfort and feelings of closeness to Julie. Sometimes I'd lie on her bed hoping for a sign that Julie was ok and praying that my world would be fine again. Neither wish came true.

After a few months of sneaking into this forbidden room, rummaging through her closet and enjoying looking at her clothes. She was so stylish – quite opposite from when she was a little girl who only wanted to wear pants and a t-shirt. I finally got up the nerve to try on some of my favorite outfits of hers. I would get sad thinking how we would never be able to go shopping or learn how to coordinate my outfits.

I did get comfort in putting her sweaters on and having them touching my body. Of course, the sweaters that formed nicely to her full breasts just hung on my underdeveloped chest. Julie was 5'4"; I was 5'7" and without Julie's curves, they hung straight down. I would never be able to carry them off with Julie's flair.

One day I stumbled across the leather purse she carried the night of the accident tucked away on the top shelf. Dad must have put it there for safekeeping. I remembered how proud she was buying this expensive purse with her own money. The tan leather had tiny flowers embossed around the edges and I started to run my fingers over them before I saw the specks of dried blood splattered on them. A haunting feeling came over me and I suddenly pictured the mangled car and lifeless bodies of Julie and friends crushed in the wreckage. The emergency people couldn't identify Julie or the others immediately because the force of the crash must have thrown the handbags around the wreckage.

I opened the clasp slowly to peek inside. Just like her room, the handbag was well-organized – wallet with friend's pictures (*thank God we had her senior picture, the last picture we would ever have*), plastic holders for insurance cards and her social security card, her Holston's employee badge and a compartment for lipstick, the only make-up she carried. Her smooth, clear complexion required little help from make-up. I carefully placed the handbag back on the shelf. Now it was just a thing in the closet. Like everything else in her room, it could give me no reason for this horrific tragedy.

Mom could not deal with anything from Julie's past so her bedroom door remained closed for over a year after the accident, except for my private visits. Finally, Karen and I convinced Mom to let us go through Julie's things. Mom refused to help – or even enter the bedroom – but we viewed this as a milestone in her recovery.

I'd already decided which outfits to keep and which to send to Goodwill. Karen seemed puzzled by how quickly I made the "to keep" and "to toss" selections. I never shared my secret visits with her or Mom. It would always be my secret.

Our time going through Julie's things was bittersweet. We laughed about some of her outfits or shared stories of our younger years. "When did she ever wear these shoes?" snickered Karen, picking up a pair of 4-inch, cork-heeled, wedge sandals. "I have no idea, but I'd be ten feet tall if I tried to wear them." I responded.

We found some old pictures of the three of us and had to laugh because Julie always had a scowl on her face when pictures were taken. "Luckily she had a beautiful smile on her senior picture," Karen said. Then we both fought off tears.

We filled eight large garbage bags with Julie's clothes. Old school papers were discarded, but every photograph of her short life was lovingly placed in albums. They would never be discarded.

Shortly after we cleaned the room, Mom allowed me to move in. The first few weeks were awkward, almost like I was trespassing. I replaced her pictures with my own, but the pale, yellow walls and gold carpet remained. I remember thinking that allowing Julie's room to have life again was a monumental step in Mom's progress in coping with her death. Mom seemed to be beginning to accept that she could hold onto the memories of Julie's short life and discard the tangible objects of her life without betraying her. Discarding Julie's clothes didn't lessen our love for her, the memories would stay in our hearts forever.

CHAPTER 19
SURVIVAL

No matter how often I tell myself I should share my feelings about Riverview with Eric, I don't. And that's exactly how it was so often after the accident.

Even though our family was making some progress in dealing with Julie's death, I still couldn't tell Mom and Dad how much I was hurting. They were too emotionally vulnerable, so I acted like everything was ok. I went to school every day, came home, did my homework and went to bed. I got straight A's and hoped each A would somehow help

Mom and Dad to focus on the future, not dwell in the past. Even my academic success failed to penetrate their apathy.

Although there were a few outward signs that Mom was beginning to accept Julie's death, it was still clear she was having trouble coping. Dad just seemed to be withdrawing. I just felt like an empty shell, but couldn't add to their grief by talking about my difficulties coping at school. Sometimes in the halls classmates passed without speaking, but still conveyed their sorrow for me. I hated that look. I imagined myself outside my body, looking at the scene dispassionately. I didn't want their sympathy. They had no idea of the emotions raging within me. I just wanted to feel normal.

Home was not a refuge. It had never been easy for Mom, Dad or me to discuss our real feelings or ask for help. Julie had been the one exception. She wasn't afraid to show her emotions or talk about things out in the open. I had always envied that ability because I always held everything inside. Now I was afraid to admit I needed help to deal with Julie's death and make some sense of this terrible catastrophe. Now I just wanted to get through one day at a time – to not hurt any more. I didn't want to think about the future; it could be taken away too quickly. I didn't want to hurt any more.

I couldn't talk to Mom about my needs. Just mentioning Julie's name sent her into a total meltdown. She even began to stutter when she tried to talk about Julie. It had always been difficult to talk to Dad because of his hearing impairment. You could never be sure if he really heard what you were saying; often he'd just nod in agreement. After Julie's death he kept his feelings to himself, easing his pain by drinking. He might have talked to Mr. Gibson about his heartache, but never to me.

Mom dismissed therapy, saying, "They'll tell me to move on with my life. I don't want to hear other's sad stories." She was devastated and refused to even consider any possibility of getting better. Sadly, that was my reality.

I read books about coping with tragedy and once read that "grief can be like breaking a bone, if not set right it aches forever." I began to believe this was the way it would be and so I began to look for comfort in school.

I bounced around from one person to another, trying to find someone or something to make me happy. I was searching for a confidant, someone who would understand my sorrow, who would allow me to release my pent-up grief. Few people would be comfortable in that role. And if anyone finally did muster the courage to ask me about my family or my sister, I'd break down. Obviously, unburdening yourself about your parents' depression and your sorrow was not the way to expand your social circle.

I did feel comfortable with my long-time friend, Lori. She knew us before the accident so knew how Mom used to be and saw the change in our family. And her mom had my deepest gratitude for her help the day of the funeral. But Lori had a steady boy-friend and didn't have a lot of time for me.

I also started to look outside school and when I turned sixteen I took a job as a cashier at a local discount store. That was partly rebellion; I chose not to work at Holston's. But even that show of independence didn't help with my insecurities about my physical shortcomings. I was 5'7", weighed 100 lbs., flat-chested and very shy so didn't attract many boys. Still I enjoyed going out with some of my coworkers. Any diversion from my home life was helpful.

CHAPTER 20
A SYMBOL OF LIFE

When we drove past Marion High for the fifth time on our Riverview visit, I resign myself to the mixed feelings the building triggers. After that October night, it was difficult to remember how excited I was the summer before my sophomore year. I couldn't wait to go to Marion High, one of the top ranked high schools in the state and home to over two thousand students from 10th to 12th grade. These were supposed to be my glorious high school years. I was proud to be the Neuman girls' little sister because Karen and Julie were so popular. I just knew these would be happy years.

After the accident, I'd always be the sister of one of the girls' killed by a drunk driver. I can't erase the memory of how that night changed those years.

The news of the worst fatal accident in the history of Chester County spread quickly through school. Support from teachers, counselors and students who knew, even superficially, Julie and her friends was overwhelming. I was glad for this outpouring and grateful for the incredible way the school chose to make something worthwhile out of this terrible tragedy. The class of 1973, Julie's class, entered a local radio station's School Spirit contest for a cash prize. The entire student body participated and collected over 20,000 signatures in three days to win the contest.

The administration and class members decided to establish a memorial fund for Julie, Amanda, Chris, Vickie and Diane with the prize money. When word spread throughout the community, individuals, dozens of schools (even our rivals), and businesses wanted to contribute to the fund. Eventually, enough money was raised to set up a scholarship for five students who would graduate in 1974 and to build a fountain in the school's courtyard in memory of Julie and her friends. Eight months after the accident, the fountain was completed.

It was dedicated on Sunday, June 3, 1973 before a solemn crowd of 250 people. Mom didn't attend the ceremony. She was still having difficulty accepting Julie's death so Dad and I represented our family. I was sorry Mom wasn't there to see the support for Julie and her friends. Perhaps it would have helped her.

The memorial service and fountain was in the courtyard, an outdoor grassy area, where students gathered for conversation, during lunch or between classes. Now the circular, brick fountain would be a symbol for students to reflect upon the fragility of life. The five small geysers surrounding the center water burst represented the five students killed.

In his remarks, the principal said, "The unbroken flow of the central spray and five smaller geysers will enhance the fountain's symbol of eternal life." The senior class advisor described the bubbling waters as "a symbol of the vitality and verve shown by the lost classmates."

The pastor from Mathews Lutheran said in the dedicatory message, "The lights shining through the water will further symbolize love's conquest of death and will remind us how precious life is." To the senior class, who provided this gift, he simply said, "God bless you for remembering."

Each time I pass the school, I truly hope they are remembered.

CHAPTER 21
SUMMERTIME...BACK TO NORMAL

I made it through my sophomore year and was excited for summer break. I could return to the pool and it became my refuge for the summer. All my uncertainties disappeared when I was swimming. My routine was simple: swim practice, help teach swim lessons, and play tennis or Ping-Pong. Lori and I rekindled our friendship since we were both on the swim team.

Mom often took me to practice on her way to

work and I loved this time to talk on the way to the club. But I didn't think anything unusual when one day she said, "I'm going in late. Would you mind walking?"

I kissed her good-bye, packed my bag and walked to the club, enjoying the bright blue sky and chuckling to myself remembering the trick Karen and Julie played on me once on our walk to the pool. Remembering the happy times helps me mask the sorrows I feel on our trips to Riverview even when I was being teased by my big sisters.

I remember how startled I was when Karen screamed, "Ouch!"

"What happened?" Julie asked.

"That bush tried to eat me." Karen said.

"I've heard about man-eating plants," I naively said.

"They'll eat the skin right off of you." Julie replied, prompting Karen to hold out her bloody finger.

For the next several months, I went two feet

around the man-eater. I wasn't going to be bitten. They let me believe the plant was carnivorous for several months before confessing that Karen had a cut on her finger and they had made up the entire story. *Memories like this will help me keep Julie alive.*

But even as I cherish those cherished simple memories, I have to struggle to keep dark, dark memories from overcoming me. Sometimes I can't. And this day as we went past the swim club, I remember getting to the pool after warm-ups had started, peeling off my sweatshirt and shorts and diving in, reveling in the pool's tingly coolness.

When coach called me out of the pool shortly after 9:00 to take a call, I was still full of that wonderful happiness I felt when I was in the water. I grabbed my towel and rushed to the office so was a little out of breathe when I said, "Hello."

"Sammy?"

It was Mom's boss, Mr. Nelson. Immediately I sensed something was wrong.

"I'm worried about your mother," he said.

"She didn't show up for work today and she's not answering the phone."

"She said she was going in later, but I'll leave right now to make sure everything is ok. Thanks for calling."

I threw on my clothes and started home. *Why wasn't Mom picking up the phone?* I wanted so badly for my life to feel normal again, but this call brought me back to the sad reality that things would never be the same again.

Charlie Brown greeted me as I unlocked the front door. "Hey Charlie Brown, where's Mama?" I asked, petting his head as I entered the foyer. I yelled, "Mom!"

The house took on an eerie stillness as my voice echoed up the stairs.

I walked upstairs and was relieved to see her sleeping soundly. I didn't want to startle her, so I tapped her gently on the shoulder. There was no response. Mom's body was limp and when I tried pulling her up her eyes rolled back and her head fell forward like a rag doll.

"Please wake up!" I pleaded. Then I grabbed the phone and dialed 911, sobbing to the dispatcher, "Please help my Mom, she won't wake up!"

"Did your mother take anything?"

"I don't know," I replied, rather irritated. *What did it matter that she was on antidepressants? Why should I tell this stranger why Mom was on medication?* I just said, "My Mom needs help! Please!"

When the ambulance finally arrived, the paramedics were able to revive her enough to calm me and assure me she'd be ok.

As the paramedics were wheeling Mom out, Mr. Nelson called. Sobbing, all I could say was, "I thought she was dead!"

"Don't you worry, she will be ok. I'll call your Dad."

Standing in the driveway watching the ambulance speed away, I felt so alone. Once again, Mrs. Gibson came to my rescue. She folded me into her arms and walked me back to her house.

Mom had to stay in the hospital for some psychiatric evaluations. She depended on antidepressants to get her through the day and sleeping pills to get through the night. The medication allowed her to cope; it could not cure or heal the pain.

Mom's doctor met Dad and me the next day at the hospital. He and Mr. Nelson were the only people Mom talked with about her true feelings with Julie's death. She tried to hide them from Dad and me. They had both known Mom before the accident and could see her transformation since Julie's death in October.

"Your mother took an overdose of pills, but there was no damage to any organs. Physically, she should be fine," the doctor said.

"Why?" I asked.

"Everyone handles tragedies differently. Your mother is having a very difficult time. Try to be patient." *It had been over eight months, how patient do I have to be?*

I couldn't hold back the tears as I walked into

Mom's room.

"Why did you do this?"

Mom looked straight at me and cried, "I needed to be with Julie."

I hung my head and tears rolled down my cheeks. Sitting silently next to her, holding her hand, I kept thinking about the special bond Mom and Julie had. I couldn't help thinking that Mom would've handled the death better if I had been the one who died.

Even today, her words resonate in my mind. I remember thinking, once again, I'd have to deal with Julie's death on my own. I could never tell her how much I missed Julie or how I needed someone to talk with about her death and how I hated people feeling sorry for me. I couldn't even tell her how upset I was with her trying to kill herself because I was afraid it would hurt her more.

CHAPTER 22
A PLEA FOR JUSTICE

One of the memories I always try to unsuccessfully block out was the hearing at the Juvenile Detention Center. I hadn't expected all the media crews. I should have because this accident, the worst drunk driving accident in Chester County's history, had claimed five innocent lives. Of course, I was only thinking of how it had shattered my family. The disgust we felt as we walked pass the news reporters and down the dingy, cold stairwell at the Center would only become stronger as the trial proceeded.

We were the only victims' family at the hearing. *Why hadn't any other families come to show their support? Maybe they didn't want to subject themselves to additional heartache.* I couldn't believe Mom was willing to listen to all the details leading up to the crash and to face the boys who ruined our lives. But she was adamant. As painful as it would to be, she had to face the defendants. Maybe she hoped they would feel some remorse after seeing her distress and heartbreak. *But why was I here?*

When we walked past the barrage of cameras I wondered why the public thrives on other people's tragedies? I'd always felt sorry for victims' families on TV. Now we were one of those families.

My expectations of a brightly lit, wood-paneled, TV show courtroom vanished when we opened the door. The cement-block courtroom, painted a nondescript pale green, was no more than a 24 x 24 foot room.

Our lawyers sat at a table facing the judge. We sat behind them. To our right were the defendants,

James Donley and Dean Patterson, and their lawyer. Dean was in a wheelchair, still recovering from a broken leg from the wreck.

When I looked at the two boys, the cause of so much heartache, I was sickened. They were dressed in wrinkled shirts and pants and their unwashed, greasy hair hung limply, covering their necks. A vision of the beautiful, vibrant faces of Julie and her friends flashed through my mind. *They didn't even have the decency to come to court dressed in a respectable fashion.* When Mom finally got the courage to look at the boys, she grunted in disgust. I'm sure she shared my thoughts.

My heart was breaking. They showed no remorse as the judge questioned them about the night of the accident. Both were underage, yet a delicatessen owner sold them beer without asking for identification. James smirked when he told the judge he pried the bottles open with his teeth because they didn't have an opener. I watched in disbelief when his mother smiled as if she was proud of this accomplishment.

Mom couldn't hold back her emotions as the details of that evening unfolded. She wept openly – sometimes moaning – as the defendants continued their accounts.

Finally, the judge slammed his gavel down. "Ma'am, you will be dismissed from this courtroom if your outbursts continue."

Embarrassed, I quickly put my arm around Mom to calm her. She had every right to be upset. How could this judge be more irritated with Mom's outbursts than the senseless accident and lack of remorse from the defendants?

Couldn't he see Mom was completely drained, ready to collapse from the emotional strain of reliving Julie's death? How much more could she take? Thankfully, 15 minutes later the judge announced a recess to review the testimony before sentencing. The judge's final statement before clearing the courtroom was simply to warn the defendants, "I better not see you back in this court again!" Then he stood and addressed the victims' parents, "That's all folks, get yourselves lawyers and sue for whatever you can."

We just sat there in shock.

CHAPTER 23
THE VERDICT

A week later, the charges against Dean and James were announced: five counts of vehicular homicide, driving under the influence and reckless operation of a vehicle.

Although the National Highway Traffic Safety Act (NHTSA) was passed in 1970 after approximately 1.4 million people lost their lives from alcohol-related accidents from 1966 until 1970, neither this astounding statistic nor the law resulted in more stringent penalties for the two teens responsible for the deaths of Julie and her four friends. The judge originally ruled Dean would be sent to the Ohio Youth Correctional Institute. He later suspended his sentence, citing Dean's leg injury that might disable him for life, and placed him under probation. Both defendants had to:

1. Pay a $500 fine to the Juvenile Institute

2. Forfeit their driver's license until 21

3. Contribute $500 to the Marion High School memorial fund for the five victims

4. Be confined to their homes unless accompanied by a parent.

5. The judge also suggested, but did not require, that they talk with youngsters regarding the dangers of drinking and driving.

After a few years' probation, which would probably be violated, they would move on with their lives. How I wished for a more permanent sentence. I wished the judge had sentenced them to carry pictures of the five beautiful young people they killed with them for the rest of their lives as a constant reminder of the pain they caused - just as I carry the constant reminder of the loss of Julie.

For his role in the fatalities, the deli owner was charged with selling beer to a minor. The Ohio Liquor Control Board suspended his liquor license for 70 days and eventually the business closed. The community, not the law, provided the punishment.

Because the community and press joined the families to challenge the judge's lenient sentences, he convened a panel of law enforcement personnel and safety organization representatives to discuss tougher laws for selling beer to minors. I resented these efforts which just seemed like a small attempt to redeem the judge's credibility after his failure to hold these two teenagers accountable. Indirectly, much later, this accident and the resulting publicity led to the law requiring photos on Ohio drivers' licenses.

The sentencing only increased the sorrow our family and the other victims' families felt. Mom refused to accept the judge's lack of compassion and wrote directly to our senator pleading for justice.

135

Dear Senator,

As the grief-stricken parent of a daughter killed on October 21, 1972, along with four other teenagers, by 16 year-old Dean Patterson, with no punishment administered after three court sessions conducted (or I should say misconducted) by the judge, I am asking that you investigate these proceedings

This accident was listed as one of the worst Chester County had seen and the apparent lack of the follow through to punish the Patterson boy on five counts of vehicular homicide, and at least three or four traffic violations, namely speeding, reckless driving, and most important, test proven drunk driving.

As everyone wants to believe, there really is very little punishment that can be given to a minor child, but for my own peace of mind - how come after repeated warnings to the

136

Patterson and Donley boys regarding their lies during the sessions and the judge's explanation of the term perjury - why didn't the judge and prosecuting attorney file the perjury charges as was threatened?

To say we were astounded at the flippant careless manner the entire subject of the deaths of five worthwhile teenagers' lives being taken by these dropouts is putting it rather mildly. I am disgusted with the entire judicial system and outdated laws about minors driving cars like maniacs. Do we have so little concern that the judge tells five parents, "that's all folks, get yourselves lawyers and sue for whatever you can" while he lets these kids go scot-free.

I feel so strongly about the utter disregard over a senseless, cruel loss of my beautiful daughter that I am asking simply that you request a transcript of the court sessions and let me know how you feel after hearing this "comedy of errors" which was called a trial.

Much more could be written here to let you know how this entire thing has affected me, my husband, and my two surviving daughters, but I plead with you to do something to stop this judge from letting guilty minors go back out to perhaps kill five more - since the final statement by the judge simply warned the boys. "I better not see you in this court again. Since the next time you will be considered adults." How many must they kill before something is done to punish them for what has already taken place?

May I please have some answer from you regarding the mishandling of the above proceedings?

Sincerely,
Phyllis Neuman

The senator's letter placed another dagger into Mom's already broken heart.

Thank you for your letter of May 2, 1973, in which you express concern about the manner in which the trial took place. Please accept my sincere sympathy at the senseless and cruel loss of your daughter. I share your deep sorrow at your loss and also your concern that such an accident may occur again.

As a United States Senator, there is little that I can do to remedy the situation. The judicial branch of government is independent of my influence. I have, however, sent a copy of your letter to the Chester County Prosecutor and have requested that he respond to your questions raised in the letter. With regard to what you call outdated laws about minors driving cars, I recommend that you contact your State Representative and Senator to inform them of your concerns regarding the present state of the law. The criminal and civil laws regarding conduct on our highways are basically state legislated and therefore beyond the purview of my legislative powers.

There is little that I can do with respect to decisions made by the judicial branch of our government. There are only two remedies for the results of judicial decisions. The first, the County Prosecutor can appeal a Judge's decision. Secondly, the judge will be accountable for his decisions at the polls on Election Day. Beyond this, there is little that can be done.

Our family was the only one to file a suit against the defendants and the deli owner. An amazing number of family friends, Julie's teachers and supervisors from Holston's wrote letters to the attorney describing their relationship with Julie and emphasizing what an intelligent, caring, responsible, fun-loving young women she was and expressing their sorrow that her bright future was taken away.

Mom and Dad never discussed how they felt about the Senator's response or the outcome of the suit, but I wondered how victims' families were supposed to respond to such tragedies. Run for office and restructure the American judicial system? I remember how bitter I was at politicians who only seemed to care about "we the people" when it was convenient for them.

Should Mom and Dad have channeled their strong feelings about how poorly the judicial system handled Julie's case into an advocacy group to work for stronger laws against drunk drivers? Admirable, but was not an option for Mom. She didn't have the strength to even try to move on with her life. She was devastated; there would be no getting better.

PART III

CHAPTER 24
THE GANG

High school memories are supposed to be treasured throughout your life, stories to pass down to your children. Driving past Marion High School on our Riverview visits always brings back my struggles to move on with my life and make those happy stories to tell my kids. The emptiness I felt after Julie's death was my norm and I struggled even to feel a part of my class. The one bright spot was my friendship with Carrie, which had become very strong during our junior year. She asked me to double date with her at the junior prom.

I was pretty confident no one would ask me and when no one did, I mustered up the courage to ask someone. He was on the football team, cute, funny and popular with the "in" crowd. I wasn't sure if he said yes because he was a sophomore and thought it would be cool to go to the junior/senior prom or if he really wanted to go with me. And I didn't care. I was just happy to be going.

Carrie and I went dress shopping and I bought a simple rose-colored gown with capped sleeves, a scoop neck and gathering at the chest. I felt pretty good in my dress even thought I was still self-conscious about my figure.

I was so excited about the pre-dance dinner at Carrie's house, the dance and the picnic the following day. But the one person I wanted to be excited for me couldn't. Mom only remembered that Julie never got to go to her prom. I couldn't help resenting that Mom couldn't be involved and share my enthusiasm. Although, I finally accepted that her heartache was too great to share in my happiness.

So I thrived off the excitement of Carrie's parents. I didn't show my excitement at home because I felt guilty that I could be happy when Mom and Dad were so sad all the time. I wanted to believe good feelings were still some where inside them; they just couldn't reach them.

Carrie's friendship was the bright spot in my life, but she also hung out with a group of girls who did everything together. They were known as "the gang." and were inseparable. Brook, Beth, Christy and Carrie went to all the school activities together.

Brook was one of the most popular girls in school. She was tall, slender and her complexion could have graced a cosmetic ad. All the boys tried to be in her circle. She was nice to everyone –a quarterback or a bookworm – it didn't matter. She'd always say hi and ask how you were doing. I was so glad she was friendly to me. Of course, a few cheerleaders were jealous of her popularity, but I always thought they just wanted to be part of "the gang." Brook always seemed mature for her age and her dates were always guys out of high school.

I sat behind Brook in social studies during my senior year and I couldn't wait to get to school on Monday to find out what the gang had done that weekend. *What fun it would be to join them?* But I never expected to be included so I was really surprised one Thursday morning when Brook asked me if I 'd like to join the gang and go listen to her boyfriend's band.

Of course, I knew darn well my social calendar was clear, but I said, "I'm not sure; I'll have to check." Then I just blurted out, "That would be great!" Never mind checking my calendar!

I was a little embarrassed when I said I had to be home by 11:30, but Mom didn't like me going out on Friday or Saturday nights, especially since she only knew Carrie. Fortunately, the gang didn't have a problem with my curfew.

I felt special being in the audience, listening to Brook's boyfriend's band and talking to them when they sat with us during their breaks. On the ride home, I thanked Brook at least a hundred times for including me.

After that night, the gang began to include me in basketball games, parties and movies. Gradually, I realized I was becoming a member of the gang and began to feel like a normal high school girl with friends to call, have lunch with or shop on weekends.

CHAPTER 25
SOLO CELEBRATION

I always made sure we didn't schedule our Riverview trips around graduation. The memories were too painful. But even when we were there at other times, just driving by Marion High brought back memories of graduation activities.

The excitement at Marion High peaked at graduation; the excitement for my June 1975 graduation was subdued at my house. Even three years after Julie's death, Mom and Dad's grief had not subsided. I was looking forward to moving on; they were still living in the past.

Being part of the gang during my senior year helped me look forward. I didn't feel so alone and empty inside. With graduation approaching, Carrie, Brook and I went shopping after school for graduation dresses. Our white gowns would cover the new outfits, but graduation was still a perfect excuse for something new.

The gang dressed at Brook's house before graduation. I was just grateful I could be excited about graduating without worrying about causing anyone pain.

Brook's mom and dad were so proud of us, taking rolls of pictures to preserve the moment. The last time Mom or Dad took a picture of me was before Julie's death. Mom never asked to see any of my graduation pictures from that evening.

Graduation was at the Grand Hall, a beautiful historical theater with magnificent architecture and a history of events dating back to the 1920's. Every seat was full. It was really impossible to find a particular face, but I still scanned the vast hall, hoping Mom and Dad would be there. They didn't come and I felt so alone and embarrassed as I walked across the stage.

Two classmates who lost their lives during the past year were recognized. *I bet their parents are here.* My heart ached for those poor families and once again the cold reality that Julie never got to walk across this stage became fresh in my mind.

After the ceremony, I stood apart watching all my classmates celebrating with their families. I was grateful for friends and their families who congratulated me, but the one person I wanted a congratulatory hug from was not there. Again, I never told Mom and Dad how much their absence disappointed me.

Later Mom admitted my graduation would have been too painful for her. "I would have only been thinking that Julie never walked across that stage." *Why didn't she think of how I felt not having her there?* Dad never explained his absence, but I'm sure he was afraid to go against her wishes and face her anger.

CHAPTER 26
SPORTS CAR TRANSITION

After graduation Brook, Carrie and I remained close, enjoying the summer and looking forward to our college adventures.

Most Marion graduates stayed close, often choosing the University of Riverview. I'd been accepted there and at a college two hours away. I didn't think Mom could handle my leaving – even though we never discussed it, so I enrolled at Riverview.

I guess since we all were still living day by day,

we never discussed my plans for the future; I got no direction from Mom or Dad about college courses. Since I didn't have much self-confidence and had no idea what I wanted to do, I enrolled in the executive secretarial program. I knew Mom loved her job and thought I could start at an entry-level position after graduation and work my way up. My decision to live at home and commute was probably not the best decision for me. Living in a dorm, away from the sadness, would have been the best option for me – but not for Mom.

At least I'd still had my friends. The gang stayed in town and we spent most Friday nights together. However, Saturday night was usually date night. Carrie and Craig were high school sweethearts and their relationship was still strong. Brook had a handful of guys who wanted to date her, but nothing serious. If Brook didn't have a date, we'd go listen to the band.

There weren't any guys knocking down my door asking me out on Saturday night like my friends.

I felt it would be a long time – if ever – before I'd have a date – let alone a boyfriend. But then a chance encounter at the mall changed everything.

Since I was often at home on Saturday nights, I really looked forward to our Friday girls' night, especially listening to Carrie's stories about Craig's family and his older brother, Eric, five years older than Craig and just as good looking. He had been the quarterback at Marion, but I never attended any games when he played. But the person she described was my dream boyfriend: funny, athletic, personable, adventurous, energetic, kind, handsome, and responsible. *Why was I so intrigued by this person whom I'd never met?*

All my friends knew him. I really wanted to meet him – how much even surprised me. *Someone like him would never be interested in me. Why would a 23-year-old want to date a 19-year-old?*

Interestingly, Eric worked at Holston's Department Store just like Mom, Karen, Bob, and Julie. But they worked at the downtown store and

Eric worked part-time at the North Hills store while attending the university. Since North Hills was only five minutes from my house, it was the logical choice when Brook and I decided to go shopping after class.

I hoped we might run into Eric and when we pulled into the parking lot, Brook said, "Look, there's Eric's car." She pointed to a maroon Triumph Spitfire. He even has a cool car, I thought to myself, and my heart started racing. *Maybe I'll finally meet him.*

But we finished shopping at Holston's and I was trying to hide my disappointment when Brook called. "Eric!" Thank goodness her yell was loud enough to get his attention, but not loud enough to embarrass me. She bounced over to give him a peck on the cheek and I just stood there, frozen. I was finally about to meet this mystery man of my dreams. Could my luck finally be changing?

He was even better looking than his description – black, perfectly manicured moustache, coal black hair with just a bit of a wave, natural coloring so he looked as if he had a tan. He had a rugged look, but his eyes and smile were gentle. I just melted. He had a confident, but not a cocky, demeanor, a muscular build and at almost six feet, his height was perfect. When Brook finally got around to introducing me, I just knew he could see how nervous I was.

"Eric, do you know Sammy?"

"No. We haven't met. Hello. It's very nice to meet you."

"It's great to finally meet you," I stammered. "I've heard so much about you."

Then I just stood there, smiling at him. Even in my memories I don't know if I said anything else and I certainly don't know how long we stood there until he said, "I should get back to work."

He probably thought I was so lame.

I've always been skeptical about love at first sight, but I don't know how else to describe my feelings as he walked away. I almost collapsed in Brook's arms. "Oh my God, he is gorgeous!"

Brook just chuckled. Of course, she could get

a guy like that; I couldn't. All the popular, cute guys liked me as a friend; they never asked me out.

I daydreamed about Eric for weeks. Then one Friday night, Brook, Carrie and I stopped at Bernie's Pub, the local neighborhood bar that was a favorite last stop for Marion alums. Its dark paneled walls and wrap-around bar hadn't changed in twenty years.

I was pretty sure we'd catch the guys' attentions when we walked in. With Brook in the lead we made quite an entrance. Being a part of the gang gave me more confidence and I walked in with my head high and my blonde hair flowing down my shoulders and back. My entrance could have been a video for a country song. "She slowly entered the bar and glanced around the room. Her eyes sparkled and she smiled when she saw her prince charming across the room."

Eric was on the other side of the room playing pool. He didn't see me, but I spotted him immediately, just as my girlfriends abandoned me to talk with some of the guys. But before I could try to attach myself to another group, Eric came walking toward me and my palms turned clammy and panic started. *Oh my God, what am I going to say?*

"Hi!" he said, "Where have you all been tonight?"

I was so nervous. I was surprised I didn't break out in hives. "We're just getting back from listening to Brook's friend's band," I said. Then before I could say anything else, Brook came bouncing over and took control of the conversation. I was jealous and worried, all at the same time. *He's going to ask her out. I can just feel it.*

These chance encounters went on for several weeks. We continued to stop at Bernie's on the way home and I hoped I hid my disappointment if Eric wasn't there. When he was there, I was thrilled even though I barely spoke two or three sentences to him. When I'd get home, I'd lie in bed and listen to Carol King or James Taylor albums and fantasize about being with this wonderful person. I was too embarrassed to let my friends know about my infatuation.

I was sure they'd think I was out of my league pursuing someone like him.

Then one Saturday morning the phone rang. I answered on the first ring but didn't recognize the voice.

"Sammy? Hi, this is Eric."

I almost dropped the phone and I was definitely fighting a panic attack. Would you like to go out this weekend?"

He barely finished the sentence before I said, "Yes!"

"I thought we could go to the drive-in. If that's ok with you?"

"That sounds great!"

"I'll pick you up at 8."

Thirty-four little words – our entire conversation -- but I was so happy I didn't know if I should scream or cry. Crying won. I just sat on my bed and wept. *Dreams do come true!*

As soon as I stopped sobbing, I called Carrie to share the big news – Craig's older brother had asked me out. She was happy for me, but reminded me of his track record for dating many girls. I didn't care, even if it was a one-time date, the man of my dreams had asked me out. I was elated.

When I told Mom about my date and that Eric worked at Holston's, I was hoping she'd share my excitement, but she only said, "That's nice." I tried to dull my pain by telling myself the medications she needed to deal with Julie's death kept her from showing emotion.

When the big night arrived, I was a complete wreck. I didn't have much dating experience, especially with an older guy, and we were going to a drive-in. *What am I getting myself into? I'll be fine. He has that little Triumph so nothing can happen. What about a goodnight kiss? I hope the movie is good, so I don't have to talk too much!*

I bought a new top and took extra time getting ready. I wanted to glow on the outside as much as I was glowing inside. I still couldn't believe Eric asked me out.

The doorbell rang right exactly at 8 o'clock and I introduced him to Mom and Dad. They gave me a 12:00 curfew and we left. I was floating until I saw the car. Then my stomach went to my throat. His small two-seater Triumph Spitfire had turned into an Oldsmobile Delta 98. This car could fit three people in the front and four in the back. It was gigantic.

"What happened to your car?" I asked with concern.

"I thought we'd would be more comfortable in my mom and dad's car."

"Oh." *What did that mean? How could I have made such a stupid reply?* But then he smiled at me and opened the door and nothing else mattered. I slid next to him. It was so comforting to be next to him. I just knew this was going to be a night I would remember forever.

CHAPTER 27
THE TURNING POINT

For many years driving past the drive-in was one of the bright spots of our trips so I was sorry when we returned one year and it had been replaced with an apartment building. I can still picture that beautiful, starry night. It was warm enough for people to sit outside their cars to watch the movie, but we stayed in the car and I cuddled up to Eric. We both laughed at the same movie parts and talked about mutual friends during the slow parts. When he put his arm around me I didn't want him to ever move away. The few kisses we exchanged made my entire body tingle.

On the way to my house I thanked him a dozen times for a wonderful evening. "I had a great time, too," he said as he walked me to the door. He held me in his arms and pressed his lips against mine in a goodnight kiss. I didn't want it to end; I might never get another kiss from him.

When I lay in bed that night, I couldn't believe how comforting it was just to be near him. I prayed he'd call again and fell asleep knowing I would cherish this night forever.

Wonder of wonders! Our dating continued. But it was so sporadic I was almost always in a state of panic. He'd call, we'd go out, then no word for a week or two. Even though I hadn't dated a lot, I knew my girlfriends had problems with relationships when they'd question their boyfriends about everything they did or where they were when they didn't hear from them. So I decided to just be patient and enjoy our time together.

Eric eventually introduced me to his close friends – guys and girls – who hung out together. I was proud Eric was so popular. I quickly realized he was also an organizer – planning the next gathering or setting up golf or tennis dates.

His friends welcomed me into their group and after several parties, some of the girls told me I was different from most of the girls Eric had dated. I didn't ask what that meant, but I took it as a compliment.

Eric and his friends had a closeness that I never had with other people. Sometimes I wondered if that was because of the tragedy that took not only Julie, but also Mom and Dad from me. I had to stop myself from feeling envious when I saw how easily they laughed and joked together. The gang had become my good friends, but it wasn't the same. Eric had known some of the guys since grade school. I yearned to have had such close friendships.

Even after I was included in Eric's activities with his friends, there'd still be weeks without a phone call because of work or activities with his friends. I often turned down Friday or Saturday night outings with Carrie and Brook hoping he'd call. When he didn't, I'd get angry with myself for wasting another evening alone.

When he called, I never pressured him for a reason. My time with him was too precious to spoil. I hung on his every word. He was such a wonderful storyteller, everything he did sounded exciting.

Being with him was like having a ray of sunshine surrounding me, such a contrast to my gloomy life. Eric was my therapy. When I started to dwell on the past and talk about Julie, Mom or Dad, he guided me toward a bright future. I couldn't help feeling guilty around Mom and Dad because there was no way I could hide my happiness.

Every time we were together was a new adventure – water skiing, motorcycle riding, snow skiing, and camping –new experiences I had found only through Eric. He made me forget about all my sadness and feel special. I was slowly beginning to believe Eric cared for me, but I never took him for granted.

And that's why I was devastated, but not surprised, when my world shattered one day when we were at one of my favorite picnic places. We were lying on a blanket and Eric was teasing me about always having to do most of the talking. Then he turned toward me and became very serious. "Sammy, you're too young to be getting serious with me. You have so much to look forward to and so many opportunities to meet different people."

I wanted to cry. *I knew it was too good to be true. He didn't want to go out with me anymore.*

"Eric, you're the only person I want to be with. When I'm with you, I feel so safe. All the sadness is washed away. I have never been happier in my life." *Oh my gosh! I said it. I can't believe I let those words slip out.*

"I just don't want you to regret missing out on anything." Eric said.

"How can you say that? You've shown me a

169

whole new world. Please can we still go out?" *Oh my God, now I was begging. He doesn't realize how he makes me feel. I'm so afraid of losing him.*

Eric stopped me, holding up his hand, he smiled and said, "I still want to go out with you."

And so we officially became a couple.

We'd been dating steadily for almost nine months when Eric accepted a job with a logistics company and decided to rent an apartment with a friend.

He worked twelve-hour shifts – seven days on and seven days off. When he worked 7 p.m. to 7 a.m., he'd sleep until 2:00 or 3:00 p.m. so he had free time before his next shift. My classes at the university were over by 2:00 and I couldn't wait to spend those few hours with him. They were the highlight of my day.

One day in October 1978, Brook and I went shopping after our morning classes and I bought a sweater for Eric. I couldn't wait to give it to him. I was working on my homework and when the phone rang around 3:30 I jumped up to answer it, blurting out, "I bought you something today when I was shopping with Brook." Instead of the expected thank you, there was a pause. Then he said, very calmly, "I was in an accident, I'm in the hospital."

Suddenly I was reliving Julie's accident. It had been such a wonderful day just like the one that preceded Julie's accident. I just wanted to be with him.

"What hospital are you in? I'll be right there." I asked the right question, but I was so distracted I didn't listen. I simply rushed to St. Simon Hospital. At the information desk, I asked for Eric Dawson's room.

The elderly lady leisurely scanned the screen. I had to resist turning the computer around to look up the room myself when she said, "There's no Eric Dawson here."

I turned and ran from the hospital crying, trying to think where the ambulance would have taken him. *How could I have been so stupid – wasting valuable time by going to the wrong hospital!* Edwards

Hospital was about five miles away, less than a mile from his apartment; I drove there.

I was still crying when the receptionist said he was in room 192. Finally, I'd be by his side. I took a deep breath and slowly opened the door, then rushed to his bed. Only after I hugged him did I realize his mother and father were there.

Eric had an IV and his arm was wrapped from his wrist to his shoulder. Machines were monitoring his vitals. Bandages covered his nose and his eyes were bruised and swollen. Seeing him like this, I couldn't keep my composure and burst into tears. As his eyes welled up, he said, "I'm ok."

"What happened?"

"I was almost back to my apartment around 7:45. I must have fallen asleep and crossed the centerline. I ran into another car."

Fortunately, the other driver was unharmed. After my initial terrifying reaction, I realized because he had fallen asleep his body was relaxed. This probably reduced the severity of his injuries; the officer at the scene said it was a miracle he had survived. Eric was wearing a seatbelt and I was grateful for this added protection, but I couldn't help thinking that a seatbelt wouldn't have protected Julie.

My entire body ached for the pain he was in and I was frustrated because there wasn't anything I could do. I didn't want to leave his side, but knew I should let his parents have some time with him.

When I got home and started to tell Mom about the accident, the blood drained from her face and her body tensed. She shivered from a cold chill down her spine. I was sure she was upset about Eric's accident, but her reaction was clearly triggered because her mind immediately flashed back to Julie.

"Please don't tell me anymore. I just can't hear about this."

Even four years after Julie's accident any news that brought back memories of the horrific night was still too hard to bear. Once again, she couldn't comfort me. I would handle major events in my life by myself.

Eric's elbow surgery was scheduled the next day and he stayed in the hospital for three more days. My daily visits to the hospital seemed to perk him up, something that seemed to disconcert his mother. She was shocked when Eric said I'd be taking him home. I was thrilled!

His arm was in a sling, not a cast and I had to be very careful helping him in and out of the car. That's when I knew I wanted to take care of him for the rest of my life – whether he knew it or not. Then as I fumbled to unlock the apartment door he leaned against me and quietly whispered, "I am going to marry you some day."

Was it the medication talking? Did he want me to hear him? I didn't care. I locked those words in my heart, although I never mentioned them to him. I would never give up on him. *Someday, this man of my dreams will marry me!*

CHAPTER 28
A GOOD FRIDAY

If I only think about my life after I met Eric when we're in Riverview, happy memories can sometimes offset the unhappy ones. That's why I have such a vivid memory of the Good Friday dinner when Eric joined us.

Our traditional Good Friday meal was always a big deal. Dad would prepare his special fish dinner. We'd eat in the dining room from our fine China and crystal. A homemade dessert recipe passed down from my paternal grandmother, Holland Rusk

Pudding, capped off the meal.

I always thought Dad's hearing loss was part of the reason he was so passionate about cooking, especially preparing holiday meals. When more than one person was talking and the conversation became jumbled, he had difficulty hearing. Cooking alone in the kitchen kept him from being frustrating afternoon and seeing everyone enjoy his meals made him feel a part of the group.

Of course, I wanted this evening to be perfect for Eric. When I was with him, the pain and sorrow I'd been dealing with since Julie's death seemed to disappear. His confidence and optimism uplifted everyone around him, especially me.

To ensure a flawless evening, I insisted Mom follow some ground rules. The one subject strictly off limits was Carrie's engagement to Craig, Eric's brother. She couldn't ask Eric when we were going to tie the knot. Not only would this have been totally embarrassing, it would put unnecessary pressure on him. I was confident he would ask me to marry him when the time was right.

Eric was one of the few people who could lift Mom's spirits, telling stories about common acquaintances at Holston's that made her laugh. It was so wonderful to see signs of the fun-loving person that Mom was before Julie's accident when she talked to Eric.

Eric's favorite phrase was "Every day is a good day" and he truly lived by it. He didn't let things bother him. He enjoyed life and was helping me to do that too. I wished Mom could adopt Eric's attitude.

Dad pulled off another culinary delight and in typical fashion just shrugged and said, "It was okay" when we all raved about it. He knew darn well how delicious the meal was; he just wasn't going to brag.

The evening had gone well. Mom had not mentioned Craig's engagement, so I relaxed. Then Eric said, "Phyllis, what do you think about my brother and Carrie getting engaged?"

I was shocked!

"Well, Sammy didn't want me to say anything,

but…"

Oh no, here it comes.

"I was hoping you'd propose to Sammy before your brother and Carrie were planning their wedding!"

I was so embarrassed. I could feel my face turning red.

Eric's answer was simple. "I don't know how to respond to that."

I stood up and said, "I do. We need to go!" I wanted this conversation to end.

I kissed Mom and Dad good-bye. Eric gave Mom a hug, shook Dad's hand and thanked them for a wonderful meal. As soon as I got in the car, I blurted out, "I am so sorry about my Mom's comments."

"You don't have to apologize. Really, it is okay."

I dropped the subject immediately. No sense in making it worse. But on our quiet ride to his apartment I had plenty of time to wonder what he was thinking, but was afraid to ask. *I wished he would at least say something.*

Eric unlocked the door and I walked in, just like so many times before. He closed the door and said quietly, "Sammy," capturing my hands. I expected a soft kiss, a gesture to assure me that Mom's comments didn't matter. Instead, standing in the doorway, he asked, "Sammy, will you marry me?" and placed a ring on my finger.

The man of my dreams, the man who showed me how to live and laugh again, wanted me to be his soul mate. I wanted to freeze that moment – the beginning of our lives together – in time.

CHAPTER 29
TEEING OFF

I can't ever pass Cherrywood Country Club without smiling. Yes, it's in Riverview. Yes, Riverview is the scene of so much tragedy, but there are only happy memories at Cherrywood. Even when I dread our visits, I look forward to Cherrywood. This visit is no exception.

I remember how brightly the sun was shining on that September day in 1981. Mom and Dad were beaming with joy on the outside, hiding, at least for this day, their sorrow, but I knew they were thinking how beautiful Julie would have looked walking down the aisle. I refused to let any memory of Julie's death mar this day.

The weather was perfect, all our early concerns about an outdoor ceremony were banished. We'd be married in the serenity of the beautiful golf course where Eric and I had spent so many happy times.

Karen's wedding had been beautiful, but so big. I had always dreamed of sharing this special day with only close friends – Eric agreed. We spent hours reading various verses to create our personal vows. Our Unitarian lady minister was perfect for our non-traditional ceremony. We did not have a best man or maid of honor. Eric's two brothers were groomsmen and Carrie and Karen were my bridesmaids. My six-year-old nephew was the ring bearer.

The groomsmen wore cream-colored tuxedoes that complimented the bridesmaids' peach colored dresses. My dress had a fitted lace bodice covered in a cream-colored shear silk and the skirt was a single layer of satin with a silk overlay. I wore a brimmed, silk-flower trimmed hat tilted to one side, a perfect complement to my Twiggy haircut.

Eric and I refused to alter our daily routine. We were not superstitious. Eric kissed me good-bye as usual when he left for an early tennis match, although we did agree not to see each other again until the ceremony.

Carrie and I met Mom at the clubhouse to go over final arrangements. Mom seemed to be handling all the happy activity well, but I knew she was crying inside. I remember hoping she wouldn't retreat into her sadness after Eric and I left for our honeymoon.

I arrived at the first tee in a decorated golf cart, driven by Dad, and smiled at the crowd – some seated between the evergreen hedges, others stand-ing along the evergreens.

When I stepped out of the golf cart and stood at the end of the white runner, I looked at Eric for the first time since this morning and my heart stopped. He looked spectacular. I held Dad's arm and walked to the altar, locking eyes with Eric. We knew this was truly the right thing to do. At that moment, I was the happiest person in the world. All my sadness over the past years just disappeared.

As Eric and I expressed our love for each other, my eyes and heart were totally focused on him. I didn't look at Mom and Dad; I didn't want to see any tears and wonder if they were tears of joy for me or heartache for Julie. I refused to let any remorseful thoughts tarnish the most important day of my life. Eric would be there for me in good and bad times and would do everything possible to make me happy. My wedding day may not have been the culmination of an elaborate fairy tale, but I truly believed I was living a real life happy ending.

CHAPTER 30
THE PURPLE SURPRISE

Even our return trip to Charlotte doesn't mean the memories stop. Driving back, I can remember driving over the bridge shortly after our marriage after Eric accepted a promotion and we moved to a suburb outside of Buster, Ohio. I was thrilled to start a new life and leave the past behind me.

Eric traveled about 30 miles to work; my commute to my new job as an administrative assistant at InfoTech was much closer. I took advantage of the company's tuition reimbursement program and started working toward a bachelor's degree. I had an associate degree, but I realized I needed a four-year degree to advance my career. Eric's encouragement made it easy for me to juggle work and school.

Everything seemed to be falling into place and then nine months later InfoTech closed my division – but rehired me a few months later as a customer-training representative.

Eric was in charge of both sales and operations and worked ten-to-twelve hour days. Work and school limited my free time, too, but we still found time to socialize with friends, play golf and take spontaneous weekend trips.

Eric continued on his upward career path and after three years was promoted and we moved back to Riverview. I had reservations about moving back and stirring up all those memories, but was supportive because it was necessary for Eric's future. I had to postpone my studies, even though I only needed six more credits to complete my degree, but was confident I'd reach this goal someday.

Once again, Eric's promotion came at a good time in my career. I'd completed my sales training and there happened to be an open sales territory in Riverview. My career goals were falling into place.

When we told our families we were moving back, they were overjoyed.

We bought a three-bedroom ranch on a private drive. The wooded backyard was perfect for entertaining family and friends.

Life couldn't have been better. We both had successful jobs with opportunities for future advancement. Again, we enjoyed weekend getaways, parties with friends, tennis and golf matches – but mostly we just reveled in being together.

By the time we moved back, most of our friends were having their second or third child. We always answered queries about parenthood by saying we weren't thinking about a family in the near future. I could never erase the picture of Mom and Dad's pain after Julie's death. Frankly, I wasn't sure I wanted to have children and never forgot to take my birth control pills.

But one day, I stopped at the drug store for a couple items on my way home from work and because my period was late I picked up a pregnancy test. *There is no way I could be pregnant.* Then the pink strip turned purple. After the room stopped spinning, I recognized fear. I was scared to think how I would handle having a child of my own and how our lives were going to change.

I remember that when Eric got home I simply said, "My period was late so I bought a pregnancy test. It turned purple."

He looked confused. "I thought you were on the pill."

"I am, but I think we're having a baby!"

He gathered me in his arms and we cried.

Once we were over the shock, Eric and I realized what a blessing this was and how excited our parents would be. Still I waited another month before telling our parents and work. I was very fortunate that I had an easy pregnancy – no morning sickness – and worked until two weeks before my July 15, 1986, due date.

We'd already started to curtail social activities, but the week before my due date the doctor said I had a couple more weeks so Eric and I decided to host an All-Star Baseball Game party on July 15th.

It was sweltering the day of the All-Star game and I went for a swim at Cherrywood. Just being there made me happy because of the wonderful memories of our wedding.

I got home around 3 p.m. to make Skyline Chili Dip, White Castle sandwiches and straighten up the house. I didn't get very far when suddenly I felt a little cramping. These were different from my regular cramps and were short bursts lasting ten seconds. After two hours of these bursts, I called my friend, Katie, a nurse and my go-to-person for medical issues.

"It might be the start of labor pains," she calmly said, "just relax and time the contractions. Give yourself a few more hours to see if they get stronger" I hesitated to call the doctor. He thought I had a couple more weeks.

By five thirty, I was sure these were real contractions and we cancelled the party – except for insisting Katie and her husband come over. I wanted her medical knowledge and their parental experience; they had three children.

At 8:30, we called the doctor. He said to call when the contractions were five minutes apart. Eric wasn't happy with the advice. Around 10:30 the contractions were getting stronger and closer. Katie was trying to keep Eric and me calm, but it wasn't working. Eric didn't like seeing me in pain. We called the doctor again and this time he said go to the hospital. Katie assured us everything would be ok as she sent us on our way.

When Eric asked if he should call Mom and Dad. I screamed, "No, I only want you there with me!"

I don't tolerate pain very well, and they were unwilling to give me an epidural until my contractions were closer. I spent several hours crying and begging Eric to have them give me something. Finally I got the epidural and relaxed. Eric was amazed when the monitor spiked during a contraction and I remained calm.

I dozed off for a little while, but when I woke, it was time to push. Tyler Eric Dawson, 7 lbs. 13oz and 21 inches long, made his appearance at 7:35 a.m.

After that exhausting night of labor, I needed to get some sleep and Eric went home to announce Tyler's birth. But the drama wasn't over. I slept deeply for a few hours, woke and tried to get out of bed. I fainted. I was quickly hooked to an antibiotic IV to combat an infection and very high fever. Then the nurses said there was a problem and they couldn't bring Tyler to my room. They didn't tell me why and I called Eric in hysterics and begged him to come.

Finally, the pediatric nurse explained that Tyler had turned blue that morning and was being monitored more closely in the neonatal care unit. He also had a higher than normal level of jaundice and needed sun lamp treatments. We had to wear gowns and masks to see our son and were warned that the IV and wires connected to his little chest were just precautionary – only to monitor his vitals. That warning didn't help. Eric and I burst into tears when we saw our little Tyler lying there helpless.

Less than 24 hours since Tyler's birth and we were already dealing with our first crisis. *How am I going to do this?* Holding Tyler in my arms, I suddenly understood – at least partly – why Mom and Dad were so devastated over the loss of Julie. I refused to even consider anything happening to Tyler, and I couldn't keep myself from wondering how Mom and Dad would deal it.

The special unit had limited visitation so our visits were much too short. And like Tyler, my post-delivery time wasn't the usual one or two days. Because of my infection and fever I stayed in the hospital four days and still had to go home without Tyler. We were frustrated and felt guilty about leaving him and so relieved when we finally got to bring Tyler home two days later. Our joy with Tyler was mirrored in Mom and Dad. Their new grandson brought back some of the happiness that had been stripped away from them fourteen years earlier.

When my eight-week maternity leave ended, I realized caring for Tyler was more important than my career. Remembering how I wished Mom had been home when I was a little girl, made my decision to stay home much easier.

I knew I had made the right decision to stay home, but it wasn't easy. Tyler was colicky, Eric was working longer hours and traveling, our easy-going lifestyle was now just a memory. We didn't regret these changes because we were so grateful Tyler was healthy and loved him so much.

But when a part-time sales job came up when Tyler was nine months old, I went back to work. I had the best of both worlds: I worked three days a week (I really loved the stimulation and challenge), I had a capable, reliable women to care for Tyler who lived just a couple blocks from Eric's mom and dad, who volunteered to pick up Tyler if I ever ran late.

Best of all, Tyler settled into his new routine.

PART IV

CHAPTER 31
THE BUG BITE

Sometimes we detour on our way home and the extra time in the car lets me remember how happy we were after Tyler's birth. I was finally beginning to put all my sadness away. Mom and Dad seemed more like the loving, concerned parents from my childhood. I couldn't wait to celebrate Mother's Day, 1991, with a picnic at our favorite park.

Both sets of grandparents would be there – even Mom, who usually avoided wooded areas. She complained that bugs attacked her. I hoped we'd get through the day without an incident.

When we packed up leftovers, I asked Mom to babysit on Friday. Her quick yes and happy smile raised my spirits. Tyler had really made a difference in her life – and Dad's. He especially liked taking Tyler to their backyard lake to skip rocks. Tyler would spend Friday night with Mom and Dad. When Mom came to pick him up on Friday, I was just finishing my make-up.

"It'll be another 10 minutes," I said, turning to walk to my bedroom. Mom followed me to the bedroom and said, "I think a bug bit me at the picnic Sunday. Would you take a look at it?" She lifted her top and exposed her breast. I was shocked. This was no bug bite.

The nipple was inverted, the breast was dimpled like the skin of a grapefruit and the entire area was red.

I'd never seen anything like it. "Mom, you have to call your doctor immediately and have this checked out! When did you notice this?"

"It was a little red on Monday after the picnic. That's why I thought something bit me. Then this morning, it looked like this." I tried not to show my concern. I didn't want to worry her, but I was really scared.

"Do you feel ok? Are you sure you want to take Tyler home with you?

"Absolutely! I am fine."

Having him around would probably be a good distraction.

Mom's doctor worked her in Monday afternoon. He and Mom had a long history. He'd been her physician since before Julie was killed and played a major role in helping her physically and mentally after the accident. I made arrangements for Tyler so I could be with Dad for the examination. When the doctor called us in, I could tell the news wasn't good, but was still shocked when he said, "Your mother has breast cancer."

"How could that be?" It seemed to happen overnight."

"There is a certain type of breast cancer that can suddenly show up without any previous symptoms. We'll run some tests and do a biopsy. Don't get too worried until we determine what we're dealing with."

Why Mom? Hasn't she been through enough? She just seemed to be coming to life again after Tyler's birth. She was just beginning to share my happiness.

I thought Mom and Dad needed some time alone and I wanted to see Eric. He'd gone to his parents' house to pick up Tyler and we'd planned to have dinner with them. But as soon as I walked in Eric knew something was seriously wrong. He took me into another room and I burst into tears and told him Mom had breast cancer. We left immediately. He'd call his mother later and explain.

After the biopsy, Mom and Dad met with the oncologist. The news was worse than we'd imagined. Mom had stage four inflammatory breast cancer, a rare form that affected only 1% of breast cancer patients. They couldn't tell us what caused the cancer, but the doctor said cancer could often be triggered from trauma. Once again that tragic accident so many years ago would devastate our family. Once again my happy memories were overshadowed by sadness.

Mom was surprisingly calm when she told me the diagnosis and the proposed treatment. They would remove the left breast then aggressively attack any remaining deadly cancer cells with chemo and radiation. Her positive attitude, so different from previous reactions to bad news would be a blessing. It would keep her strong throughout this ordeal.

I spent hours searching the Internet to learn about inflammatory breast cancer. The results were always the same. At stage four the survival rate was very low. Aggressive chemotherapy and radiation were the only chance for remission, but it would likely reoccur.

Even though the data was depressing, it helped me understand what Mom was facing and, surprisingly, that knowledge about this new challenge for our family comforted me. I never shared my research with Mom. Instead, I just concentrated on keeping a positive attitude to keep up Mom's spirits.

Too bad the ability to access information on any subject wasn't available in 1972. I might have gained some insight on how to cope with Julie's death.

Within two weeks of finding the cancer, Mom's left breast and lymph nodes under her arm were removed. Chemo started before the incision healed. The oncologist felt confident that Mom's history of never smoking or drinking would allow her to withstand this aggressive chemotherapy regime despite being sixty-eight. Radiation wouldn't start until after the doctor evaluated the chemo's success.

Mom was impressed with her young doctor's knowledge and felt comfortable in discussing her struggles coping with Julie's death. I believe he was moved by her tragic past and I sensed a special bond between them. There were no complications from the surgery but there were cancerous cells in her lymph nodes. She declined reconstructive surgery and I was impressed how the surgery didn't seem to affect her self-esteem.

When I could, I'd drop by the oncology center when Mom was having her chemo treatment. Most days, she'd be nicely dressed, her hair or wig styled, fresh make-up, and manicured nails, which she showed off so the nurses could admire the one nail adorned with a little flower or other design. Other times, however, she was too weak and simply put a scarf on her head and wore comfortable warm-ups for her trip to the hospital.

When she was feeling good, we'd talk about Tyler and Eric and my happy life while the chemo slowly dripped into her veins washing away the cancerous cells. I know my being there was comforting her. It was also therapeutic for me. It gave me back some time with the caring mother of my early childhood. She looked at me – and not through the lens of Julie's death.

Mom struggled with all the chemo side effects – loss of hair, nausea, fatigue, mouth sores, and change in the taste of food. She rarely told me how sick she really felt. Sometimes when I'd call, she'd just say she was tired and we'd talk later.

Ironically, Mom and Dad were finally enjoying each other's company again. Dad took her to her doctor's visits. When she was feeling well enough, they'd go out to eat or just for a ride in the country, stopping at fresh fruit and vegetable stands or a country store to pick up special treats for the nursing staff. After Julie's death, they had grown apart. Now another crisis was bringing them back together.

CHAPTER 32
RENEWED LIFE

After Eric and I moved back to Riverview, we often visited Karen and her family in Willowbrook, a suburb of Chicago, until they moved to North Carolina. I remember thinking that if they hadn't moved I would have been living in the same town with Karen for the first time since we were children when a job opportunity for Eric opened up in the Chicago area. Although they were gone, we were familiar with the area because of those visits. The timing was good as Tyler would be starting first grade in the fall, Mom's cancer was in remission, and she and Dad were enjoying their time together. I was worried about not being there for Mom if her cancer returned, but I was also glad to once again leave all my tragic memories behind.

We found a house in a new development in Willowbrook. The elementary school was within walking distance; children could walk or ride their bikes to school. There were baseball fields, tennis courts, a fishing lake and a clubhouse with a pool and waterslide.

Eric and I approached every move as a new adventure and looked forward to exploring a new city and making new friends. Life was good. I continued to heal from the trauma of my high school and early adult years. When people asked me about my family, I was hesitant to even mention Julie for fear they would feel sorry for me. Once again that time in my life was tucked away.

We moved in the summer of 1992 and I established a ritual of calling Mom every other day.

These calls kept me up-do-date on Riverview and Mom always seemed eager to hear about our activities. But after six months Mom told me her cancer had returned. It started with pain in her legs, which doctors first said was probably side effects from the chemo and radiation. When the pain continued, she went to the oncologist and after additional tests, he confirmed the cancer had returned, this time in her bones. Her only treatment choices were additional chemo to slow the cancer's progression and powerful pain medication. We knew she wouldn't be cured, but would buy her some time. She chose chemo. She wasn't giving up.

I wanted to be there for Mom, but I had to take care of my family. Eric knew I was stressed, but he insisted we take a planned a spring break trip to Phoenix in March 1993. Eric always seemed to know how to help me through life's twists and turns. He was right about the trip.

I was struggling with Mom's prognosis and trying to figure out what I needed to do. When we hiked in the desert mountains away from any distractions, Eric and I had the opportunity to talk about what was truly important in life. We decided to try to have another child, not as easy decision since my tubes were tied. After discussing our options with one of the top fertility doctors in the area, we decided surgery to retie my tubes was our best option.

Mom was more worried about this surgery than her own health problems. Worrying about me seemed to give her a reason to go on. She was strong enough to come to stay with Tyler and Eric while I was in the hospital. The six-hour surgery was a complete success.

By the summer, I was pregnant, which seemed a confirmation of our decision. The news of another grandson seemed to rejuvenate Mom's inner strength and inspire her to keep fighting. She was determined to hold her new grandson.

As the new life inside me grew, the cancer continued to eat away at Mom's body. I called her every day -- some times twice a day to talk about Tyler and his soon-to-be brother. She sometimes couldn't remember what we were talking about because the pain medication was so strong. I started writing weekly letters about my doctor visits, how Eric was doing at work, and adorable things Tyler did at school and updates about his sports. I'd always end with a motivational quote.

The cancer was spreading through her bones. She struggled to hang on to see her new grandchild, but the pain seemed to be overpowering her will to live. I needed to see her, although a five-hour road trip was not feasible. But after Dad called to say Mom wasn't doing well, I got the ok to fly down even though I was in my ninth month.

By the time I arrived in Riverview, Mom was back in the hospital. I knew she had been put on a morphine drip for the pain when the patches were no longer effective, but I really had no idea what to expect. I took a deep breath before opening the door. *I hope the shock doesn't make me go into labor.*

Fortunately, her pain was under control by

the time I got there, but she looked so frail lying there in bed. Crissy, her tiny Yorky on guard by her side, was the one thing that gave her comfort. Mom was actually more coherent than I expected. She was pale, but she didn't look like she was dying – although I wasn't sure what that was supposed to look like anyway.

She was happy to see me, but concerned about my traveling so late in my pregnancy. I let her feel the baby move, hoping this would give her additional strength, and assured her I was fine. "Don't worry about me, Mom. You just need to hang in there to see your grandson."

This child inside me gave me strength to deal with Mom dying; I hoped it gave her the motivation to fight for her life.

Once her condition stabilized, I was relieved to go back home. I gave her a long hug and kissed her good-bye not knowing if it would be the last time I saw her alive. I remember I continued smiling at her as I walked out of the room. As soon as I closed the door, I burst into tears.

I was two days from my delivery date and Mom and Dad's anniversary. She was still in the hospital as the pain continued to worsen. Dad brought flowers and cake to celebrate, but she didn't have the strength or appetite to eat.

We had two feet of snow a day before my due date and Tyler spent the day building snow forts. I'd been cooped up for two days because of the snow and when I developed a craving pizza, we decided to brave the snow and go to our favorite pizza place.

Tyler's day in the snow caught up with him on the way home and we were both ready for bed by 9. At 11:30, I woke Eric and said, "It's time. "I'm in labor!" It still amuses me when I think about how differently I handled going into labor this time.

Eric had this wonderful idea to video tape our experience and started filming me as soon as he was dressed and had finished his introductory comments.

His first question was "How are you feeling? Is there anything you would like to say before we go?"

That's as far as it went. I just said, "Eric, please turn that off, I just want to get to the hospital. Wake Tyler and tell Laura we're coming over with him."

He turned it off, called our friends and got Tyler ready while I showered.

The hospital was only a ten-minute drive. I timed my contractions and they were about eight minutes apart, which I was able to tolerate. Eric turned the camera back on to film my arrival, but by the time we were in the birthing room, I was ready to throw the camera out the window. He turned it off again. Only he and I would experience the birth of our second child.

I was given the epidural earlier and was able to tolerate the pain. We both dozed off for a little bit. Around 6:30, it was time to push. Brad arrived at 7:30 on February 27, 1994. We had decided to call our parents after the birth instead of in the middle of the night. The first person we called was Mom. The phone in her hospital room rang three or four times before she picked up, saying groggily, "Hello."

"Mom, it's Sammy. Guess what?"

There was a slight pause. "Are you ok?"

"I'm wonderful. Eric and I are holding our baby, Brad."

"You had your baby!" She said and started to cry.

"We're all doing great! Hang in there. You're going to get to see your new grandson soon!"

We learned later that a friend visited her that afternoon and was surprised to find her sitting up eating cake. Dad said the friend, who didn't know about her new grandson, blurted out, "You're supposed to be dying!"

"Not until I see my grandson!" she replied.

Three weeks later, Brad was in Mom's arms and she was sitting in her wheelchair in the sunroom at her house.

Her turnaround stunned the doctors and nurses. They had never seen a patient so close to dying rebound like this. Brad truly was a blessing for our entire family from conception to birth and beyond.

CHAPTER 33
FULL CIRCLE

We only have a few more hours on the road home. It's been a quiet trip, filled with happy and sad memories. As we travel the last miles I find myself contrasting the summer of 1973 when Mom had tried to end her life with the spring of 1994, twenty-two years after Julie's death, when she was fighting for every breath to stay alive. But we knew she would not win this fight. The breast cancer, after two years in remission, metastasized to her bones. She no longer controlled her destiny.

Each daily call to check on Mom from March through June 1994 became more difficult. I could tell from the slurring of words that her condition was deteriorating; she required more and more pain medication. She often repeated words and sentences or lost track of what we were talking about. I tried to be encouraging, reminding her of how lucky she was to have time with Brad.

I kept hoping Mom would open up to me about how she felt about dying or give me some words to hold onto, but they never came. She never had any comforting words for me when Julie died. Why did I hope for some now that she was dying?

As her illness progressed, Mom and Dad agreed she would remain at home and contacted Hospice, a tacit admission of her fate. Hospice was truly a blessing in her final months. The daily visits gave Dad a chance to get away for a couple hours while the nurse tended to Mom.

For Mom's birthday, June 13th, Dad bought a beautiful sapphire ring. Tiny diamonds surrounded the stone. When Dad told the sales clerk about it being Mom's birthday, but that she was dying, the sales clerk had to hold back her tears. Mom wept uncontrollably when she opened her present.

Only a few weeks after that happy occasion, Mom couldn't get out of bed and the doctor recommended she go back to the hospital. Dad said they held each other and said their goodbyes before the ambulance arrived. They both knew she would never come home.

When Dad called and said, "I had to put your Mother back in the hospital. You need to come home as soon as possible."

I remember packing our suitcases and thinking, I can't believe I'm packing my black dress for a funeral. She's hasn't died yet. I feel so guilty. *Am I giving up? This could just be another scare. She may still rally.* But even as I hoped, I knew from Dad's voice it was the end to her long struggle.

That drive seemed twice as long as the usual five hours. Like other trips back to Riverdale, it was silent, except for Eric's attempts to relieve the tension. We dropped Tyler and Brad at Eric's parents before heading to the hospital. Tyler was seven and wanted him to remember his grandmother during happy times.

When Eric and I arrived at the hospital, the morphine drip was keeping Mom as comfortable as possible, but she knew we were there. Eric hadn't seen Mom in several months and tried to hide his shock at the changes. There was no doubt, the end was near.

Dad looked exhausted and I insisted he go home to get some rest and let Crissy out, reminding him that Mom always worried about Crissy and would want him to go take care of her.

"What's Crissy going to do without me?" mumbled Mom.

"How about if I take care of her, Phyllis?" Eric joked.

In her sedated state, Mom slowly blurted out, "Oh, no, don't let Eric take Crissy! He doesn't like animals."

"Don't worry, Mom. Eric isn't going to take Crissy. Dad needs her to keep him company." I said.

"Ok," Mom said, closing her eyes and falling back to sleep.

Eric had to get back to work and I stayed in Riverview with the boys. I felt guilty being away from them so much since I spent so much time at the hospital. Fortunately, they were in good hands with Eric's mom and dad.

When Karen came the next day, she joined Dad and me in our final vigil. Eventually the morphine couldn't effectively control the pain and I kept hearing those anguished cries from the night Julie was killed. We sat helplessly by her side as her organs began to shut down and she slowly drifted into a forever sleep.

Watching Mom fighting for every breath, I wondered if she was holding on for Karen and me. She worried about us even though we both had wonderful loving husbands and families of our own. *In*

221

some way could this be her trying to make up for the times when I needed her and she couldn't be there for me? I wished she could let go.

When Karen and I realized it was the time to say our final good-byes, Karen spent several minutes alone by her bed. When she slowly walked out of the room in tears, I went in. Sitting next to Mom on the bed, I watched her every breath. Each one was a struggle. There were long pauses and my heart almost stopped each time. *Is this her last breath?*

Even in her comatose state, I knew she could hear me. I'd rehearsed my last conversation with her. I was going to tell her how since that October night in 1972, I wished it had been me, not Julie in that car. I was going to tell her I knew Julie was her favorite and believed she would have handled the accident better if I had been in that car. I didn't say any of that. What good would it have done? I would continue to keep all those feelings inside me.

Instead I said, "I will miss you, but be okay. You don't have to worry about me. You know how happy Eric, Tyler and Brad make me. Eric will take good care of us. It's time to be with Julie." I kissed her on the forehead. "I love you. Thank you for everything you did for me."

Perhaps the reasons my last words were words I hoped would comfort her came from another death. A few days before Mom's death, a dear friend lost her father suddenly from a heart attack. I went to his funeral from my last hospital visit. I remember thinking this family, much like ours when Julie died, had no time to prepare for this death. They didn't have a chance to say good-bye. In some strange ways I was fortunate; I had months of grieving to prepare for Mom's death and show her how much I loved her.

After the funeral, I had debated about stopping at the hospital again. When I'd left after my final words, the nurses said her vital signs were failing and she probably wouldn't make it through the night.

It was about 10:30 and had been such an exhausting day, I just wanted to be with my boys. I drove past the hospital. The boys were sleeping, but

I held them tight and wept. To this day, I regret not making that last visit to the hospital.

Karen was staying with Dad and they had gone to bed early, exhausted after this emotional, draining day. When the phone rang around 4:30 a.m., Karen ran to answer it. Silence was the only response to her hello. She held the phone for a few minutes and then hung up. Twenty minutes later, the phone rang again. Karen was still awake thinking about the previous call. It was the hospital. Mom had died around 4:35. When the phone rang, I took a deep breath knowing it was the call.

"Mom's gone." Karen cried.

"Was she alone?"

"No, Rick was there."

Mom called Rick "the vampire" when he came to the house to draw blood and they'd developed a friendship during the six months he cared for her.

He'd been at the hospital and stopped by her room about 4:30 and was with her in the room when she took her final breath. He told us, "She finally looked at peace." Knowing that someone she trusted was with her in those final moments was comforting. Mom was no longer suffering over Julie's death or from the pain of her cancer. She was at peace and finally with Julie.

AFTERWORD

My husband and I have been married for 37 years and I'm grateful every day that he rescued me from that sorrowful time in my life.

My boys are now grown and starting their own journeys. I love them so much and I'm so proud of them. The oldest is practicing law and married to a wonderfully talented artist and counselor in Charleston, South Carolina and the other is pursuing a career in supply chain management and going to graduate school in Raleigh, North Carolina.

My Dad moved to Florida a year after Mom died. He passed away in 2010 from colon cancer and was there when he took his final breath. I remember being thankful that he would no longer have to deal with his hearing impairment. His struggle to accept Julie's death was finally over and he was reunited with Julie and Mom. I could now be at peace.

EPILOGUE

After so many years of suppressing these dreadful memories, I realized I was glad that I allowed myself to confront them. I was beginning to feel a sense of peace. We're heading away from Riverview and back to Charlotte, and the tension is subsiding. I'm so grateful to be returning to my life of love and happiness with Eric.

I'm ready to tuck my memories away for now and hope when they return they won't be as painful. Deep down, I know they are forever etched in my heart and soul as vividly as the day they happened. I know when I sit on my patio listening to the peaceful sound of our fountain, I will always be reminded of the water that continually flows down the courtyard fountain of Marion High School in memory of Julie and her friends. I will be grateful that Mom is with Julie. But now I believe I have finally conquered those memories.

"Regardless of what life throws at you, persevere to find the happiness you deserve."

Tammy Ward